C000246061

Field Guide to the
BUMBLEBEES
of Great Britain & Ireland

Sponsored by ENGLISH NATURE

Field Guide to the
BUMBLEBEES
of Great Britain & Ireland

Mike Edwards | Martin Jenner
Bumblebee photography by Ted Benton

This book is dedicated to the memory of Howard Street

First published by Ocelli, March 2005
Reprinted April 2005
Reprinted November 2005
books@ocelli.co.uk
www.ocelli.co.uk

Created and produced by Formula Creative Consultants
© In text by the authors
© Bumblebee photography Ted Benton
© Bumblebee anatomical photography and line drawings
   Martin Jenner
© Diagrams, symbols and icons Formula Creative Consultants

ISBN 0-9549713-0-2

Printed in England by Dexters

Photography
All bumblebee and bumblebee mimics by Ted Benton. Habitats
and bumblebee anatomicals by Martin Jenner. Bumblebee's nest
by Paul Westrich. Conopid fly by Robin Williams.

Illustrations
Life cycle by Tony Hopkins. Line drawings by Martin Jenner.
Front Cover: Male *Bombus lucorum*.

Opposite:
Female *Bombus jonellus*.

Acknowledgements

The authors would like to thank the following:

First, and foremost, Dr. David Sheppard of English Nature for his encouragement and support in all things to do with bumblebees. English Nature for their financial support of this book. Ted Benton, who supplied photographs of all the bumblebee species shown in this book. Ted also kindly shared his knowledge of bumblebees. Dr. Paul Williams of the Natural History Museum and Dr. Murdo Macdonald who kindly checked and tested the Identification Chart. Murdo and Scottish Natural Heritage for kindly agreeing to our adaptation of the Bumblebee Names chart. The Bees, Wasps and Ants Recording Society (BWARS), especially Stuart Roberts, who provided much of the map data. Colm Ronayne and Tomás Murray who supplied distribution data for Ireland. Tony Hopkins for allowing us to use his illustration. Dr. Paul Westrich and Robin Williams for use of their photographs. Alan Bond for allowing us to use the studio insect photograph. Howard Street who contributed towards the editing. Formula Creative Consultants for producing the concept, and Dean Pavitt for the design. Keith Deal for his invaluable help. The authors' wives: Maria Jenner and Sue Edwards, who not only proof read the text but remained calm, patient and supportive during the whole production process. Last, but not least, Andrew Branson of British Wildlife for his kind suggestions.

CONTENTS

INTRODUCTION

WHAT ARE BUMBLEBEES?

Bumblebees are large, colourful and attractive insects which are familiar, well liked and completely harmless to most people – they are more likely to roll over on their backs than sting you. Bumblebees are one of the first insects to be seen in the year and their buzzing is one of the evocative sounds of sunny days during the months of spring and summer.

True bumblebees are social insects, where the dominant and reproductive female – the queen who has mated in the late summer – emerges from hibernation in the early spring to form a new colony. After finding a suitable nest site she rears her first offspring – workers – who are also female but who do not reproduce other females, and their sole function is to forage and care for the colony. Workers have similar coat patterns to the queen but are much smaller. Later on in the season males and new queens are produced. Male bumblebees often have different coat patterns from the females (sexual dimorphism). These do not hibernate and die off at the end of the season, usually in late summer and autumn, as do the workers and the old queen. The new queens, after having mated, hibernate over the winter and form new colonies in the following year.

There are a group of bumblebees called cuckoo bumblebees, which are parasitic on social bumblebees and often resemble their host. The female cuckoo bumblebee, who is large and powerful, usurps a social bumblebee's nest – dominating or killing the smaller and less powerful queen – and then appropriates the workers to care for her own offspring. She does not produce workers, but produces new females and males in the late summer. The new females hibernate during the winter months. Cuckoo bumblebees were formerly a separate genera with the scientific name *Psithyrus*; they are now grouped together with social bumblebees under the genus *Bombus* with *Psithyrus* being a sub genus.

Bumblebees are related to hive or honeybees and do produce honey but this is only on a very small scale. The queen bumblebee in the early spring produces a small solitary honey pot to get the colony started. Interestingly, there are historical accounts of country children stealing the thimble sized pot of honey from bumblebee nests in hay meadows.

Whilst many people are generally familiar with bumblebees and enjoy their presence, few have knowledge of their identity as individual species, nor are they aware of their importance as pollinators of fruit trees, wild and garden flowers; and even some arable crops. There is also little awareness that bumblebees are seriously threatened and declining – one species has even been declared extinct in Britain in the last few years. Concern for bumblebee welfare by scientists and entomologists has led to much preliminary research – providing important evidence on the reasons for their recent decline and some conservation action to remedy this, but further research and more conservation action is needed.

As with any group of animals, accurate identification of an individual species – as obvious as it may seem – is key to the success of any ecological research and a requisite for taking conservation action. Without this, and the many amateur and professional fieldworkers who provide species records, little of our wildlife and their habitats would be conserved or protected today.

Despite their popularity, there are few books on identifying bumblebees, and most of them require some scientific knowledge before they can be used successfully. Whilst we recognise the importance and role of these works, and even recommend some of them for further reading, one of the main functions of this book is to make the task of identifying bumblebees easier, especially in the field.

The field guide is aimed at conservationists, scientists, nature reserve and park wardens, amateur naturalists, and to encouraging anybody who is interested in knowing more about bumblebees. We do hope that it will help towards a greater understanding of bumblebees, encourage more research into their ecology and also promote further conservation action.

10

HOW TO USE THIS BOOK AND ITS CONTENTS

The Field Guide to the Bumblebees of Britain and Ireland is intended as an introductory work and, with practice, you will be able to identify with confidence most of the 22 known species. A few bumblebee species, in particular workers, are difficult to identify even by experts; these are highlighted in the species sections.

There are several ways in which users can begin to recognise and determine individual bumblebee species with this field guide. You can start by using the photographs, which show both sexes of all the currently known species in Britain and Ireland, and then follow with the accompanying species notes. Alternatively, the Quick Identification Chart which uses body colour patterns and notes on obvious structural characteristics is also very helpful in giving decisions on an identification. For those who have some knowledge of bumblebee species and their identification, the habitat and seasonal icons, together with the distribution maps, provide important clues to a species' identity. To get the most accurate results, however, it is ultimately more effective to combine all the identification information provided and the book is designed to be used in this way as a cross-referencing system.

One of the main differences between this and other specialised insect field guides, which mostly use sequential taxonomic keys – and require dead specimens – is that the user has the choice of where they may begin in the guide to identify a species. Using the guide in this way does not require the killing of specimens – the usual requirement when identifying difficult insect groups. There is, however, a section on 'Going further' at the back of this book, which provides a more scientific identification method using photographs of the female bumblebee basitarsi and male bumblebee genitalia, which are useful in confirming determination of both sexes.

The book also contains outlines of the latest bumblebee research, biology, life cycles and foraging behaviour; notes on habitat management and conservation. There is also a section on how bumblebees can be attracted to gardens – with a chart of suitable forage plants you can introduce – and how they can be tempted to nest in gardens.

USING SCIENTIFIC NAMES

In the interest of bumblebee ecology and conservation, we consider it vitally important that all interested parties start using the same language to avoid the kind of confusion amongst the general public and the media which results in inaccurate statements and identification. The problem is that, of the 22 species of bumblebees that currently exist in the UK each can have as many as three different so-called 'common' names. See Table 3 on page 101. And since these 'common' names – like the Large Earth Humble-bee, Buff-tailed Humble-bee, Buff-tailed Bumblebee (all known scientifically as *Bombus terrestris*), are mainly the inventions of different authors and not in common usage by the general public or the media, we will refer to each species *only* by the internationally-accepted scientific name.

If this sounds a little daunting, it's worth bearing in mind that children have no difficulty in using the scientific name *Tyrannosaurus rex* when referring to a dinosaur... *Tyrannosaurus* the name of the genus... *rex* the name of the species.

All bumblebees belong to the *Bombus* genus – so it is only the second part of the scientific name that will change for each particular species, e.g. *Bombus lucorum* and *Bombus pratorum,* which can also be shortened to *B. lucorum* and *B. pratorum.*

So how do you pronounce these strange-sounding names? Since they are primarily for written communication and derived from ancient languages which are no longer spoken, it doesn't really matter how you pronounce them.

What is important is that the use of these scientific names will best serve the interests of getting a clearer and more accurate picture of bumblebee populations and habitats by making sure that everyone is using the same language when referring to a particular species.

Scientifically bumblebees belong to the insect order Hymenoptera, which forms the largest order of insects in Britain and Ireland with over 6000 species. Interestingly, there is no English collective name for Hymenoptera – unlike Coleoptera (beetles) and Diptera (flies). Within the Hymenoptera, bumblebees are part of the division Aculeata (ants, bees and wasps). More specifically, they belong to the family Apidae (bees) and are fairly closely related to hive or honey bees.

As with any group of species – in particular, insects – there are often differing taxonomic opinions on what are actual individual species. Sometimes, with closely related species, advanced knowledge of a species' morphological structures and its ecology can subsequently result in a 'splitting of the species' and then a further one is discovered and named. With the development of genetic research this has made the task of what constitutes a species a little easier. For example, *Bombus lucorum* may be made up of three separate but closely related species: *B. lucorum*, *B. cryptarum* and *B. magnus*. Recent genetic research is likely to eventually confirm these are indeed three separate species.

This field guide goes to species level of bumblebees only, and does not deal with sub species in any detail. Thus, we deal with *B. lucorum* as single species and treat *B. magnus* as another possible species found in the North. In addition, the identities of the pair of species known as *B. hortorum* and *B. ruderatus* have long been a subject of disagreement amongst entomologists – including the authors! The weight of modern evidence and the existence of consistent differences in genetic markers (Ellis, 2004), supports the separation of these two species and we deal with them separately.

12

Bumblebees lead fascinating lives and they, together with other social bees, are probably amongst the most advanced and sophisticated of insects in the world. In Britain and Ireland their overall life history has been well known for over 100 years. FW Sladen documented his observations in some detail in 1912, and these give intriguing insights into bumblebee behaviour. However, much emphasis on the behavioural study of bumblebees, in the past, has been as a group rather than as individual species. Although several species of bumblebee are fairly closely related less is known of individual species' ecology (autecology). The potential danger here is that a reliance on any research based on 'lumping a group together' may not be in the best interest of individual species when taking conservation action. More research is needed, therefore, on bumblebee autecology.

Whilst social bumblebees may have different habitat, forage and nesting requirements, and even subtle differences in the way some species rear their young, the basic life styles between species, however, are similar, as are the basic life styles of cuckoo bumblebees species. There are even similarities between social and cuckoo bumblebee basic life styles, and cuckoo bumblebees have probably evolved from social bumblebees through exploiting selfish behaviour.

LIFE CYCLE

Queen bumblebees emerge from hibernation between March and May depending on the individual species, weather conditions and the geographical location. *Bombus pratorum* and *B. terrestris* are two of our earliest species, and new queens of these species can sometimes be seen as early as February in southern counties, especially if there has been a warm sunny spell of weather. Emergence of individual species of bumblebees is later the further one travels north.

Once a fertilised queen has emerged in the spring, her first task is to replenish her loss of body fats – used up during winter months of hibernation – with pollen and nectar from suitable flowers. You can usually tell when she is doing this because there will be an absence of a pollen load in her pollen basket (corbicula, which is situated on the female hind tibia). At the same time the queen also needs the pollen and nectar to develop her ovaries.

After she has refuelled, the queen's next task is to find a suitable location for a nest to found the new colony. Whilst there may be plenty of nest sites, it is the quality of the surrounding nectar and pollen sources that are critical to the rearing of the first workers. These, together with a continual forage source, are essential to the future survival of the queen and the colony. It is quite common in spring time to see queens flying low to the ground or crawling amongst vegetation as they inspect potential nest sites.

The nest site chosen is usually in a warm situation and needs to be well insulated; for example, old mouse and vole nests are ideal. These may be in a hole in the ground or on the surface depending on the species and the suitability of the site. *B. terrestris,* as its name suggests, usually nests underground. Carder bumblebees, such as *B. pascuorum,* usually nest on the surface and are known as carders for their habit of carding or combing moss or dead grass. Some species will even use old birds' nests, usually in rotten trees or nest boxes. *B. jonellus* has been found using an old Long-tailed Tit's (*Aegithalos caudatus*) nest in a gorse bush.

Once the nest site has been selected the queen makes the honey pot from secreted wax, which she fills with regurgitated nectar. This will provide her with a food source during inclement weather and whilst she is brooding her first young. Over the same period of two to three weeks, the queen collects pollen to form a large pollen lump which is a little bigger than her body. On this she lays a few eggs. These hatch into the larvae which become the first workers. In order to speed up their development the queen lies across the pollen lump and incubates it, even buzzing her wings to generate more heat.

The larvae go through several moults and then produce a silken cocoon where they pupate. After a few weeks the first adult workers emerge from their cocoons. They are usually very small in relation to the queen. It takes a little time for the newly emerged worker's coat of hairs to dry and about a day for its wings to harden sufficiently for foraging duties.

The workers' role is to take on nest and foraging duties. The nest duties include building new cells, feeding larvae and helping new workers to emerge from their pupae as well as keeping the nest tidy. Foraging provides food for the colony, which needs both nectar – principally food for the adults – and pollen for the developing larvae. In the meantime, the queen's role is to lay the next batch of eggs.

Bumblebees will fly up to 400 metres or more from the nest to find forage resources and can generally find new supplies if needed. However, there needs to be suitable foraging areas throughout the entire life of the colony, usually between April and September. Any loss of major foraging sources, such as over grazing by sheep and cattle, silage making, strimming or the practice of topping grasslands, can have disastrous consequences on bumblebee colonies and populations. While the workers are engaged in nest and foraging duties, the queen concentrates on producing more offspring. The workers produced later are bigger than the first workers but are usually smaller than the queens. The number of workers in a

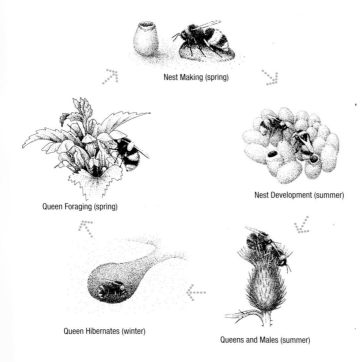

Nest Making (spring)

Queen Foraging (spring)

Nest Development (summer)

Queen Hibernates (winter)

Queens and Males (summer)

Life cycle of bumblebees

Foraging
The queen emerges in the spring, feeds and then gathers pollen and nectar.

Nest Making
The queen finds a suitable cavity and begins to make a nest of her own. She stores nectar in a nectar pot to provide food for herself during bad weather and builds a pollen larder to feed her brood.

Nest Development
The brood become workers and gather pollen and nectar to feed the later brood.

Queens and Males
Later in the year females (queens) and males are produced in the brood. They leave the nest and mate with queens and males from other nests.

Queen Hibernates
The old queen, the workers and the males die in late autumn. The new queens excavate underground chambers where they hibernate.

Bombus pascuorum colony in purpose made
nest box with introduced synthetic nesting
materials. © Paul Westrich.

colony varies depending on its success and the species type; in some species it is possible to have up to 150 or more workers in a bumblebee colony, in others as few as 40.

Towards the end of the season some of the eggs laid by the fertilised queen develop into new queens rather than workers. Should for any reason the queen be lost to the colony, the workers, although not fertilised, can also lay eggs but these always develop into males. Queens also produce males, usually at the end of the season when they come to the end of the sperm stored in special organs from mating during the previous season. Once males and new queens have been produced the colony has essentially served its function. The males, after having mated, die in the late summer and early autumn, as do the old queen and the workers.

Following emergence, the new queens may stay around the nest for a while. Eventually they mate and forage, building up their body fats for hibernation. They seek a suitable hibernation site, which can be in north facing banks, beneath the bark of rotting trees or underground in open grasslands. Little is really known of the specific requirements or the behaviour of social bumblebees during the hibernation process and virtually nothing is known of cuckoo bumblebees' hibernation behaviour.

There is now growing evidence of some bumblebee colonies over-wintering. Fresh queens, especially *B. terrestris*, have been seen gathering pollen during the autumn with regular sightings of *B. terrestris* workers, mainly near gardens, in the southern counties of Britain in December and January. It will be interesting to see

The Conopid fly *Sicus ferrugineus*.
The larvae of this fly are internal parasites
of bumblebees. © Robin Williams.

whether this phenomenon becomes more frequent. In central and southern Europe some bumblebee colonies, in particular those of *B. terrestris*, are known to over winter. The occurrence of the same behaviour here could be due to climate change.

CUCKOO BUMBLEBEES, PARASITES AND PREDATORS

A young social bumblebee's nest, possibly with few workers, is a very valuable prize for queens who haven't managed to found their own nest, and several studies have shown that battles over nests occur between queens. One group of bumblebees has evolved to specialise in this activity: the cuckoo or social parasite species. Cuckoo bumblebees may specialise in parasitising one host species, or may choose a number of closely-related species. Cuckoo bumblebees often have to fight to take over nests so they usually look bigger than their hosts but they often resemble them superficially.

Female cuckoo bumblebees emerge from hibernation approximately six weeks after the host species. When the female cuckoo has found a suitable colony, she creeps into the colony and hides amongst the edges of the nest canopy for several days. Once she has acquired the scent of the nest, and been accepted by the workers, the cuckoo then either dominates or kills the queen to prevent any more of the host's eggs being laid. The female cuckoo will then lay all subsequent eggs and the workers, which develop from the original queen's eggs, help to tend the young male and female offspring of the female cuckoo bumblebee. Cuckoo bumblebees never produce workers. After emergence the new cuckoos leave the nest. Having mated, the male cuckoo bumblebees die before the winter sets in; the females then go into hibernation over the winter months.

Bumblebees, like most insects, have several parasites. Some of these have rather gruesome ways of parasitising their hosts. Conopid flies will wait near a foraging area until a bumblebee flies close by; the conopid then launches itself towards the bumblebee and jumps on its back. During this process the fly manages to lay an egg inside the bumblebee's abdomen. This develops into a larva that feeds on the contents of the host.

Conopid larvae are known to affect the behaviour of bumblebees: if you see a bumblebee crawling around on the ground and apparently incapable of flying, it may be parasitised. A study by Christine Muller *et al* 1993, 1994 showed that worker bumblebees, when parasitised by the conopid fly *Sicus ferrugineus,* did not return to the nest at night, although they foraged during the day as usual. This behaviour was found to slow down the maturation of the conopid larva, sometimes causing it to starve to death. Larvae which completed their development inside the bumblebee's abdomen, however, induced the host to dig into the ground, where it dies, leaving the conopid larva well protected for pupation. This is not the case for all conopid flies, however. An end-of-season nest of *Bombus hortorum,* removed from beneath a shed, was kept as an exhibit. The following spring a number of adult conopids (*Physocephala rufipes*) emerged from the nest. Clearly, some of the dead worker bumblebees removed with the nest were holding conopid pupae in them.

There are other internal parasites (endoparasites). Certain roundworms will infect bumblebees, multiply within and feed in the intestinal system. There are also external parasites (ectoparasites) such as the very small mites which live inside the breathing tubes (tracheae) of bumblebee adults. You can often see much larger mites on bumblebees when they are foraging for nectar and pollen. These mites are usually clustered in large numbers round the thorax of the bumblebee: they are not parasites but act as scavengers in the nest and are beneficial to the bumblebee colony.

Some insect parasites feed on the bumblebees' pollen stores (cleptoparasites). As the cleptoparasite larvae develop, they may also feed on the cell contents, which include young bumblebees in their pupal stage. One such species does this: *Mutilla europea*, the female of which looks like a large furry ant. The family Mutillidae are sometimes known as Velvet Ants and, like bumblebees, belong to the order Hymenoptera.

The detritus in the nest is also another food source and *Volucella bombylans,* a large hoverfly which superficially resembles a bumblebee, has a larva which survives this way without appearing to harm the host; it may even be beneficial to bumblebees by keeping the nest clean. Wax moth larvae also feed on nest detritus. They eat the pollen store, larvae and pupae. They move around the nest creating silk web. Eventually they overwhelm the colony.

Bumblebees have few other natural predators. Birds such as Flycatchers, Tits and Hobbies are known to take them; Bee Eaters (as their name suggests) regularly catch and consume bumblebees. None of these is likely to pose a serious threat to established bumblebee colonies. Badgers, however, tell a different story: a bumblebee's nest provides a very good food source, and they will commonly dig out nests, and eat the larvae, adult and provisions of bumblebees, destroying the colony in the process. It is not known what impact this has on bumblebee populations as a whole, but bearing in mind that their nests often give off a strong scent and Badgers have an acute sense of smell, it is likely to be serious. It is unlikely, however, that Badgers have contributed to the general decline of bumblebees and they should probably be seen as bumblebee predators, providing a natural balance in nature. Hedgehogs are also known to destroy bumblebee nests, which can also have serious effects on local populations.

DISTRIBUTION AND STATUS

There is evidence to suggest that some of our seriously threatened species of bumblebees today were plentiful in the past. Entomologists up to the Second World War rarely bothered to record the presence of bumblebees in their accounts. For example, *Bombus sylvarum* was known to be widespread in England and southern Wales. Comments such as '*Bombus sylvarum* everywhere as usual' (Hallett 1928). The presence of most species in provincial museums' collections bears testimony to their ubiquity. Free and Butler (1959) in their work, clearly had personal experience of most of the bumblebee species in the British Isles, whilst Alford (1975), writing 20 years later, was unable to give first hand experiences for many of them.

The results of a bumblebee mapping scheme that collected data up to 1976 and was published during 1980 (IBRA 1980) appears to confirm that many species were not so widely distributed as previously thought. In the mid 1990s the Biodiversity Action Plan (BAP) – a government backed initiative – was being formulated; this also happened to coincide with the beginning of the seriousness of bumblebees' decline being recognised.

Accordingly, five species of bumblebee were put forward as potential BAP species: *B. distinguendus, B. humilis, B. sylvarum, B. subterraneus* and *B. ruderatus.* One of these – *B. sylvarum* – was chosen for the first field studies in 1997, mainly because of its former widespread distribution and reliability of identification.

It was already known that *B. sylvarum* appeared to show a decline in the 1970s (see map overleaf) and was rarely seen during the 1980s, but the results from the first field studies, after six person-weeks of searching, were alarming: only two workers were found.

In response to the preliminary findings, the Bumblebee Working Group was set up by five key organisations: Countryside Council for Wales, English Nature,

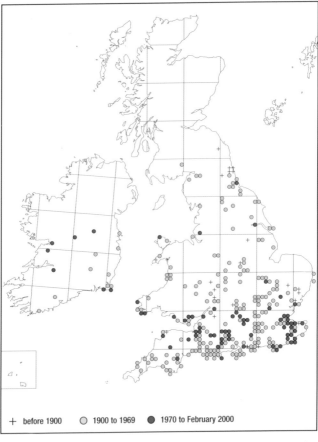

+ before 1900   ○ 1900 to 1969   ● 1970 to February 2000

Bombus sylvarum: Distribution map from the Provisional Atlas of the aculeate Hymenoptera of Britain and Ireland produced by the Bees, Wasps and Ants Recording Society. Post-1990 records would show an even greater decline!

Scottish Natural Heritage, RSPB and WWF(UK) to further investigate the status of *B. sylvarum* and the remaining four other proposed BAP species. It soon became clear that not only were these five species seriously threatened and endangered but five additional species, *B. jonellus*, *B. muscorum*, *B. soroeensis*, *B. rudararius* and *B. monticola*, gave cause for concern. Of these only *B. jonellus* was found to have widespread, albeit fairly localised, distributions with good sustainable populations. *B. subterraneus* – included in the initial surveys, but not shown in this book – formerly also believed to be widespread in southern England, was declared extinct in 2000. All of the afore-mentioned species are social bumblebees, which means that – excluding the six cuckoo bumblebees – half of our social bumblebees in Britain and Ireland are in serious danger.

Most of the bumblebee records on distribution, and much of the anecdotal evidence on their populations, indicates a major decline in numbers from the 1950s onwards. This coincides with significant changes in farming practices that included the moving away from hay meadows and their associated diverse plant communities as well as the general cessation of extended rotational cropping systems. These practices ensured, within a habitat, a provision of a continual forage source throughout the life of a bumblebee colony.

These traditional farming methods were replaced with silage making and its modern grassland monocultures, together with the common widespread usage of chemical fertilisers. The latter resulted in the ability to grow arable crops continually on the same land without the need for long rotations. This meant the end of many flower-rich communities of open landscapes which were essential for today's rarer bumblebees. Interestingly, these changes and their detrimental effect on bumblebee distribution and populations also correlate with heavy losses of the numbers of breeding farmland birds such as Grey partridges, Barn owls, Lapwings, Skylarks, Corn buntings and Yellowhammers.

FORAGING BEHAVIOUR AND REQUIREMENTS

Bumblebees will travel long distances to forage, although there is little information available to determine just how far they are prepared to go for pollen or nectar and to what extent this could affect the dynamics of the colony. What is certain is that bumblebees require a continual foraging source throughout the colony's life span. If this is not available locally they have the capability to travel further afield for it. We do know bumblebees regularly travel in excess of 400 metres radius from the nest (from research by Juliet Osbourne using radar tracking at Rothamsted Research Station).

Much modern research into bumblebees has concentrated on the economics of nectar-foraging (the bumblebees' source of fuel for energy), using the common species. This can provide useful mathematical and statistical models of energy use in relation to bumblebee flights. Pollen-foraging by bumblebees (the protein source for developing young) is however, far less studied. Such behaviour is complex and much more difficult to research but equally important, especially for

Salisbury Plain. A large flower-rich habitat of
thirty five square kilometres with large stands of
Red Clover, *Trifolium pratense,* and other suitable
bumblebee forage plants.

conservation action. The question for conservationists is not necessarily how a
bumblebee can travel 400 metres from the colony without a net loss of energy,
but why it does so.

All bumblebees forage from a number of different plant families (polylectic).
However, we also know that amongst bumblebee species there are individual
preferences for pollens (Carvell *et al.* 2003). Recent preliminary research on pollen
preferences has also shown that there are significant differences in the protein
content of pollen from different plant families. Goulson. D, (pers comm). Clearly,
the protein content will have an impact on the development of bumblebee young.
We know, for example, that when commercially reared bumblebee colonies start
to fail the first remedy is to change the pollen source.

The usefulness of bumblebees in pollinating agricultural and horticultural
crops was known at the beginning of the 20th century and several species were
imported into New Zealand to help establish clover-based pastures to support
and develop sheep and dairy farming. Interestingly, one of those introduced
species, *Bombus subterraneus,* has recently been declared extinct in the UK and
is also declining in Western Europe. It can still be found in clover pastures in
New Zealand. Who knows, these survivors may form the stock for an eventual
reintroduction of *B. subterraneus* in the UK!

High Weald. Natural regeneration of flower-rich
meadows under the Countryside Stewardship scheme.

CONSERVATION ACTION

Our rarer bumblebees require large areas of suitable habitat; this is likely to be
in excess of ten square kilometres in order for any population to be viable. If this
sounds implausible, consider the factors involved: the size of a mature colony;
the relatively small number of potential breeding females (queens); the variety
and quantity of consistently available forage required throughout the colony's life
span; the failure rate of colonies in poor weather conditions and the high mortality
rate of queens over-wintering. Most nature reserves are not, on their own, large
enough to support viable populations of bumblebees, and only widespread
informed action by farmers, landowners and gardeners can help. What is needed
is the establishment of suitable flower-rich areas to provide the pollen and
nectar required.

These flower-rich areas do not need to be large: one or two 6m x 100m strips
within each square kilometre of farmland will give a vital lifeline to some of our rarer
bumblebees species. These areas can easily be provided by growing a variety of
cheap agricultural legumes in field margins and there is now a pollen and nectar
mix option offered to farmers under agri-environment schemes with this in mind.

Interestingly, it has been shown that growing strips of either wild flower
mixtures or agricultural legume mixes in the midst of large areas of crops can
be beneficial both to farming and wildlife. Certain insects such as ladybirds and
hoverflies, which are useful in controling some arable pests such as aphids, can
use these strips to help them reach crop centres. This is not always possible with
field margins when large crop expanses are involved. Skylarks, Corn Buntings and

Partridges also have preferences for more open habitats; and the latter's young are known to eat sawfly larvae, which can also be harmful to some agricultural crops.

Early results in trials using agricultural legumes, notably Red Clover, in field margins on Romney Marsh, Kent have been very encouraging. There was found to be a 300-fold increase in the total number of bumblebees recorded on fixed-time transect walks during the first 3 years of the trials. After 4 years, these agricultural margins lost their flowering density with a consequential dramatic fall in bumblebee numbers. This highlights the importance of a continual forage source, and the need for an ongoing programme of agricultural legume establishment within individual farms. It should be stressed, however, that whilst this type of conservation action has worked well for such endangered species as *Bombus muscorum*, *B. humilis* and *B. sylvarum*, it is not suitable for all bumblebees. For example, *B. soroeensis* and *B. monticola* populations, essentially heath and montane species respectively, are unlikely to benefit from the planting of agricultural legumes in field margins. Ideally, the type of conservation action involving legume introduction needs to be combined with the restoration of long-term flower-rich grasslands on relatively unproductive land. Local authorities and gardeners could also help by not frequently mowing or strimming flowering grassy situations and ensure that, when they do so, it is as part of a rotational management strategy.

IDENTIFYING BUMBLEBEES

Bumblebees are fairly easy to recognise and most people are familiar with them – in particular, the yellow and black striped species with white tails. There are, however, other colour patterns and a few things that can cause confusion to the beginner. Here are some points to watch out for:

- The first bumblebee workers of a colony can often be very small.

- Towards the end of a bumblebee's life span the hair colours can fade – especially in periods of continual bright sunshine.

- A bumblebee's coat can also become abraded or depleted showing the black surface structure beneath (chitin).

- There are also other insects which resemble or mimic bumblebees.

The actual look and behaviour of an insect – sometimes called jizz – often helps with an identification. With some careful observation and a little practice this becomes an important way of determining identity; especially when combined with shape, size, colour and structural characteristics. For example, in flight bumblebees make a distinct buzzing sound and their flight is slow and ponderous when compared to bumblebee mimics.

The majority of insects that mimic bumblebees are flies. Many of these are hoverflies which, as their name suggests, hover regularly; they also have a light, darting flight – unlike bumblebees, which do not hover. The so-called bee-flies also mimic bumblebees and, interestingly, are parasitic on some solitary bees. *Bombylius major,* the commonest of these, can often be seen hovering over bare ground and hedge-bottoms in the early spring. It can be recognised by its long, rigid tongue and wings with dark markings as it hovers with its front feet on the edge of a flower whilst drinking nectar.

Observing live insects closely in the wild and in a tube with a magnifying glass, or dead museum specimens under a microscope, will help you to recognise the differences in the structural features mentioned overleaf.

Bombylius major. A bee-fly common along hedgerows in the early spring. Note its long straight tongue and dark wing bars.

IMPORTANT STRUCTURAL DIFFERENCES BETWEEN FLIES AND BUMBLEBEES

Wings. In common with all winged Hymenoptera, bumblebees have two pairs of wings. Flies have only one pair. The hind and fore wings of bumblebees are connected together by tiny hooks (hamulii), which can be seen under a microscope. Recognising this feature does take experience. However, the difference does become obvious, even in the field, with a little practice.

Antennae. Bumblebee antennae are always long, thin and hairless. The individual segments are similar to each other and cylindrical. Fly antennae are variable, often short and thick with strong differences between the individual segments.

Mouth parts. Bumblebees, in common with beetles, have strong, easily visible mandibles, or jaws, which they use to cut nesting materials; cut into the larval cell to feed their young and help workers leave their larval cell; some species even use them to gain access to nectar which would otherwise not be reachable. Flies do not have mandibles. Bumblebees' tongues are hard, long, tapered and fold away, and are invisible when not being used for feeding. Some flies such as mosquitoes and horseflies have tongues which are used for piercing, but these cannot be folded away and are always visible. The majority of flies have soft tongues, which are very often pad-like.

Stings. Female bumblebees, in common with other female aculeate Hymenoptera (the bees, wasps and ants), have a sting contained within the tip of their abdomen, and flies do not. When not being used, the sting is always hidden inside the abdomen.

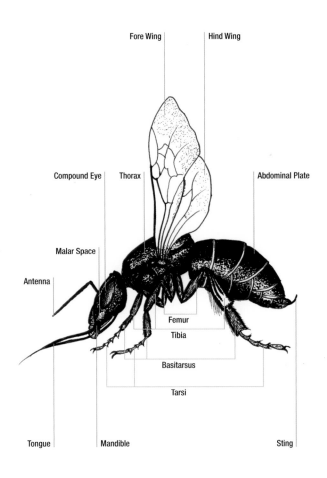

Fore Wing

Hind Wing

Compound Eye

Thorax

Abdominal Plate

Malar Space

Antenna

Femur

Tibia

Basitarsus

Tarsi

Tongue

Mandible

Sting

Main structural parts of female social bumblebee
(hairs removed)

Top: The hoverfly *Volucella bombylans,* which is a bumblebee mimic.

Above: *Meredon equestris.* A hoverfly that's a bumblebee mimic and is common in gardens.

OTHER BUMBLEBEE LOOK-ALIKES

There are a few day-flying moths which might also be confused with bumblebees; especially as they have long tongues. These tongues, when not in use, are coiled and visible beneath the head. Moths also have differently shaped antennae. Many hover and/or have coloured markings – made up of scales – on the wings; although in some case these may be restricted to the edges. Some of these day-flying moths also have conspicuous tail tufts.

Solitary bees of the genus *Anthophora* look rather like bumblebees, but are smaller (except for some first brood worker bumblebees) and are very fast fliers; they also often hover in front of flowers. A few mining bees are similar to some of our bumblebees in hair density and colouration, but they have thinner, more elongated abdomens and more closely resemble the domesticated honeybee *Apis mellifera* in both shape and size.

Once you have mastered the differences between bumblebees and other insects in the field you can then begin to identify individual bumblebee species. It may help if you familiarise yourself with the photographs of examples of such 'non-bumblebees' in this book.

A male solitary bee *Anthophora plumipes*.
The female, which also resembles a bumblebee,
is all black and does not have hairy fore tarsi.

A female mining bee, *Andrena fulva,* which is seen in springtime. Note the elongate abdomen. The male does not resemble a bumblebee.

USING THIS BOOK TO IDENTIFY BUMBLEBEE SPECIES

Once you have decided your insect is a bumblebee, most will require sexing before an identification. This is because, in some species, there may be differences in colour patterns between males and females (sexual dimorphism). You will also need to decide whether your bumblebee is a social or a cuckoo as some cuckoo bumblebees resemble their hosts.

Whilst it is perfectly possible to identify many species of bumblebee without catching them, some will require closer inspection. You can catch bumblebees using an entomological net (black mesh is best) and hold them in a 75 mm x 25 mm glass tube. For an even closer view, you can use a plunger device (see opposite) or a piece of tissue, which will restrict them in one part of the tube. Use a 10x magnifying glass to help in identification. For suppliers of this type of equipment see the list of useful addresses at the back of the book.

When catching bumblebees:

- Handle them gently.

- Keep them out of the sun.

- Do not keep them in the tube for longer than 15 minutes, preferably less. If kept in a tube for long periods, bumblebees can become dehydrated, stressed and also regurgitate their stomach contents.

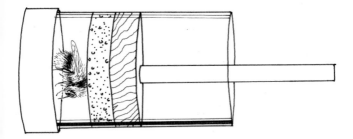

Plunger Device. Useful for close-up
views of bumblebees.

Observing these guidelines will mean that you won't harm bumblebees,
they won't harm you and you will achieve a more accurate identification.

SEXING BUMBLEBEES

This can be done easily under a microscope, but in the field it requires a little
practice and it's very helpful to use the glass tube method outlined above.

31

Here are some points to look for:

- Female social bumblebees have a pollen basket (called a corbicula) on a
  broad hind tibia. If you see a bumblebee with a pollen load (see overleaf)
  you can be sure it is a social bumblebee and that it is female.

- Female bumblebees have a sting (not visible without being extracted)
  and the last abdominal segment is very pointed – view them in a glass
  tube for this.

- Male bumblebees have an extra antennal segment – 13 in the male and
  12 segments in the female – and have obviously longer antennae than
  females. Male bumblebees also have narrower hind tibiae.

- Male bumblebees have a squared-off last abdominal segment which hides
  the genitalia – view them in a glass tube for this.

(Note: In the Quick Identification Chart and the species accounts, males, queens
and workers of social bumblebees are denoted by the the letters m,q, and w
respectively; males and females of cuckoo bumblebees are denoted by the letters
m and f.)

Female *Bombus hortorum* carrying pollen load.

IS IT A SOCIAL OR CUCKOO BUMBLEBEE?

Social and cuckoo bumblebees generally do look different from each other in the field, but the differences take a little while to appreciate.

Here are some clues:

● Many cuckoo bumblebees have noticeably darkened wings, especially females of *Bombus rupestris*. Some species of cuckoo bumblebee have a small wedge of yellow hairs at the beginning of the white tail.

● Social bumblebees are rather densely haired, giving a furry appearance. Beware specimens where the colours have faded, as these are sometimes worn and abraded. The majority of cuckoo bumblebees have much sparser hair which means the underlying shiny black body surface (chitin) can often be seen.

● The hind tibia in female social bumblebees is shiny, flat and broad with long hairs on the outer edges only. The hind tibia in female cuckoo bumblebees is dull, narrower, rounded and covered in short hairs – view them in a glass tube for this.

● Differences in the hind tibia of males are much harder to appreciate, but those of social bumblebees are shinier, flatter and less hairy than those of cuckoo bumblebees.

Hind tibia of a female social bumblebee
Bombus pascuorum.

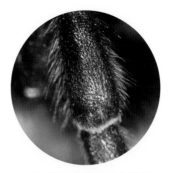

Hind tibia of a female cuckoo bumblebee
Bombus vestalis.

Hind tibia of a male social bumblebee
Bombus pascuorum.

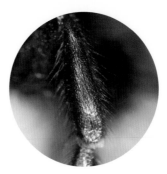

Hind tibia of a male cuckoo bumblebee
Bombus vestalis.

● The abdomen of male social bumblebees has a more rounded appearance
  when viewed from above. Male cuckoo bumblebees have blunt-ended,
  elongated-triangular abdomens when viewed from above.

Once you have determined the sex of your bumblebee, and decided whether
it is a social or a cuckoo species, you can begin to identify the species.

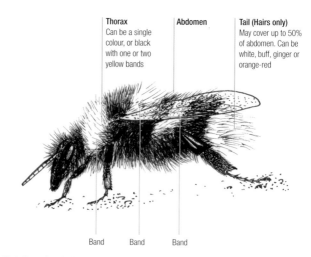

Thorax
Can be a single colour, or black with one or two yellow bands

Abdomen

Tail (Hairs only)
May cover up to 50% of abdomen. Can be white, buff, ginger or orange-red

Band   Band   Band

Illustration and terminology of bumblebee hair colours.

USING THE QUICK IDENTIFICATION CHART ON PAGES 40 AND 41

The icons are stylised both in colour and shape. Drawings of the thorax and the abdomen are separated so that you can cross reference the two to form a basic identification. You will see notes to the left of the abdomen icons. The notes in each row are numbered and refer to the species in that row and their corresponding numbers. The foot notes provide general information and also assist in identification.

Here's an example of how it works:

1. Your bumblebee has two yellow bands on the thorax. Therefore, it is in the third column.

2. It has an orange-red tip of abdomen (tail) with no yellow band on the abdomen. Therefore, it is in the second row.

3. By combining the above information, you now have a choice of four species: *Bombus lapidarius*, *B. monticola*, *B. ruderarius* and *B. rupestris*. The latter species shown in the chart is a different colour to denote it is a cuckoo bumblebee.

4. If your bumblebee is a female and the orange-red tail is more than 50%, you will know that it is likely to be be *B. monticola*. Note 1 in the first column, second row, gives you additional identification information. To check this identification you should then refer to the distribution map, the emergence diagram; the habitat icons and the species descriptions and notes on the relevant page. *B. monticola* is a montane species and only occurs on moorland in Scotland, Wales, the North and small isolated pockets in the West Country (if you found your specimen in Essex it is not likely to be this species!).

5. Suppose it is a male? If it is a cuckoo bumblebee (you will need to look closely to confirm this) you will know that it is likely to be the cuckoo bumblebee *B. rupestris* (note all the cuckoo bumblebees are marked in red on the chart). Note 2 in the first column, second row gives you additional identification information.

6. If it is a social male you have three choices: if the orange-red tail is more than 50% of the overall length of the abdomen (note 1) it should be a male *B. monticola*. If less than 50%, then it is either *B. lapidarius* or *B. ruderarius*. If the hair bands are bright yellow it is likely to be *B. lapidarius* and if yellowish-dark grey than it is likely to be *B. ruderarius*. Now check with the species accounts.

USING THE PHOTOGRAPHS AND SPECIES ACCOUNTS TO IDENTIFY BUMBLEBEES

This section is organised in order of female colour forms, not in taxonomic order, which are shown on the right hand pages. The female thorax and abdomen icons at the top of the page (the species' typical colour form) can, therefore, be used as a quick access indexing system.

You can familiarise yourself with the typical colour forms of bumblebee species by using the photographs on the species pages. Combining this information with the relevant species accounts, distribution, seasonal and habitat icons can lead to an identification. This can then be cross-referenced to the Identification chart if required.

Thorax/abdomen icons

To the side of each photograph the thorax and abdomen icons are shown. Note: on some pages the icon colours have been adjusted, when compared to the Quick Identification Chart, so that they are more representative of the individual species' true colours. Where these show more than one abdomen or thorax icon, it demonstrates the extremes of colour variation within a species. There are variations in the colours and patterns of most species of bumblebee.

Male and Female symbols

Males are shown on the left hand side and females (queens and workers) on the right hand side pages which are denoted by the letters M and F in the side margins.

Habitat icons

These should be used, as with the others, in conjunction with the grid key and photographs. They are another way of helping to confirm a species identification. For example, if you think you have found an open landscape species such as *Bombus humilis* or *B. sylvarum* in your garden, and it is not adjacent to flower rich grasslands, it may need rechecking. Below are the habitat icons' descriptions:

 Woodland, scrub and gardens

 Lowland heaths

 Mountain and moorland

 Flower-rich grasslands – a rare and often localised habitat

 Farmland and intensive agriculture

Seasonal icons

The flight periods shown in these are based on Southern England (around London). These can vary according to how far north you are. A species will emerge roughly one month later every 300 miles you travel north. Species will also emerge earlier on the south coast and/or if there is a spell of warm weather.

The emergence periods can also be helpful in identification; they are particularly important because all of our rarer and threatened species (*Bombus humilis*, *B. muscorum*, *B. sylvarum*, *B. soroeensis*, *B. monticola*, *B. distinguendus*, *B. ruderatus* and *B. ruderarius*) have later emerging queens. If you think you have seen a queen of *B. humilis* or *B. sylvarum*, for example, between February and the end of March / mid April, it is likely to be a misidentification.

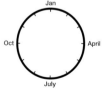
Seasonal clock

Seasonal icon

The distribution map of *Bombus distinguendus* on page 77 showing post-1990 records.

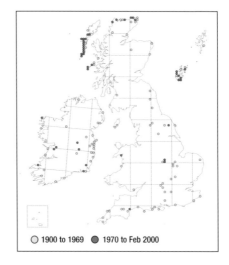

The BWARS distribution map of *Bombus distinguendus*.

○ 1900 to 1969   ● 1970 to Feb 2000

Distribution map diagrams

These can help to provide an indicator to a species' identification. Our rarer and threatened species require very large areas of suitable habitat to sustain a viable population. If you suspect your bumblebee is one of these and it is not within reasonable proximity to suitable habitat, it may need checking again by yourself or an expert. For example, *Bombus distinguendus* is now only known from North-western Scotland including the Hebridean, and some of the Orkney, Islands. Occasionally, abraded specimens of *B. muscorum* and *B. humilis* – where the black of the surface structure (chitin) shows through on the thorax – superficially resemble *B. distinguendus*. If you thought your specimen was this, and it occurred in Southern England, it would almost certainly be a misidentification.

Because of space restrictions and scale, these map diagrams only work on a one hundred km square basis and, therefore, cannot be precise. It should be noted that a distribution map can only indicate that a species has been recorded within a one hundred km square; it does not indicate the actual geographical extent of the population within it. Where possible we have provided more accurate data under the Distribution and Biology sections. The 100 km squares for Britain are based on the Ordnance Survey Grid. Ireland has been rotated anti-clockwise and moved northwards slightly in order to line up the grid squares with the British ones.

In the light of the recent dramatic decline in density and populations of many bumblebees the distribution map diagrams in this book are all based on post-1990 records which have been submitted to the Bees, Wasps and Ants Recording Society. Thus they show the modern, not the historic, distribution.

Head shape

Comparing the width to the length of the head is best done under a microscope. However, longer-faced species, which also have longer tongues, are fairly obvious in the field. To get used to appreciating this character we recommend tubing specimens as described on page 30. The diagrams which show this feature give the comparison of width to head length based on the frontal view. The difference in head shapes is mainly determined by the distance between the bottom of the compound eye and the base of the mandible (malar space). See below.

Face as long as wide.
Male cuckoo bumblebee
Bombus rupestris.

Face longer than wide.
Male social bumblebee
Bombus rudararius. Note the
mainly black facial hairs.

Face very much longer than
wide. Male social bumblebee
Bombus ruderatus. Note the
orange beard on the lower face
and mandible.

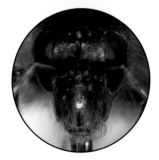

A male cuckoo bumblebee *Bombus campestris*. Males of this species frequently occur in all-black (melanic) forms.

Bombus muscorum agricolae. This sub species occurs in the Western Isles of Scotland and the Orkneys. Many island forms of *Bombus muscorum* have black hairs underneath rather than ginger-brown. The pollen load on the hind tibia also confirms it is a female.

Colour variation

Most species can vary in colour pattern occasionally. However, there are a few which regularly have different colour patterns. For example, *Bombus pascuorum* is a sandy ginger-brown coloured bumblebee which can have varying degrees of black hair patches on the abdomen. *B. distinguendus*, however, shows very little colour variation. In the UK the greatest variation occurs within some of the cuckoo bumblebees. Black (melanic) forms are known in many bumblebee species, most commonly *B. campestris* and *B. ruderatus*.

A species can be very variable in colour pattern throughout its European distribution. *B. humilis* is an all sandy ginger-brown species in the UK, whereas in southern Europe it has a black abdomen with a ginger tail. In Germany the same species is ginger with profuse dark hairs on the thorax.

Tip of abdomen orange-red
1. Orange tail 50% or more in B. monticola
2. Bands have a yellowish-dark grey look
3. Orange hairs on the hind tibia

B. lapidarius m
B. monticola m¹ q¹ w¹
B. ruderarius m²
B. rupestris m²

Tip of abdomen orange-red
1. Thorax bands are broad and all bands are pale greenish-yellow

B. lapidarius m
B. sylvarum m¹ q¹ w¹

Tip of abdomen orange-red to buff
1. Bands have a yellowish-dark-grey look
2. Tip of abdomen orange fading to white
3. First abdominal segment yellow at sides

B. pratorum m
B. ruderarius m¹

40

Tip of abdomen grey to yellow white
May be yellow hairs at the front of the abdomen but these do not form distinctive yellow band
1. Yellow side patches at top of white tail
2. Extreme tip of tail orange

B. sylvestris m² f
B. bohemicus m f¹
B. barbutellus m f

Tip of abdomen white to greyish white
1. Face as long as wide
2. Distinctive yellow facial hairs
3. Tail 40% whitish grey. Female with abdominal band sometimes faint
4. Extreme tip of tail orange
5. Yellow side patches at top of white tail

B. hortorum m q w
B. ruderatus m q w
B. jonellus m¹ q¹ w¹
B. lucorum m²
B. barbutellus m³ f³
B. sylvestris m⁴
B. bohemicus m⁵ f⁵

Tip of abdomen white to buff
1. B. lucorum, B. terrestris workers practically indistinguishable in the field
2. Distinctive yellow facial hairs
3. First abdominal segment yellow at sides

Body colour sandy yellow to ginger-brown
1. Thorax and abdomen sandy yellow; make sure the black band is hair and not wear
2. Obvious black hairs on the abdomen are always B. pascuorum

B. distinguendus m¹ q¹ w¹

Tip of abdomen ginger
1. Black hairs at tip of the abdomen. In some examples there may also be some yellow hairs at the front of the abdomen
2. Extreme tip of tail orange

B. campestris m¹ f
B. sylvestris m² f
B bohemicus m

Those with predominantly yellow facial hairs are always male in black, yellow and white species and black, yellow and orange-red species.

There are all-black examples (melanic) of many bumblebees: the two most common are males of B. vestalis and B. campestris. See page 39

B. monticola m¹ q¹ w¹
B. pratorum w

B. lapidarius m q w
B. ruderarius m² q³ w³
B. rupestris m f

B. pratorum m q w
B. rudararius m¹
B. soroeensis m²/³
B. terrestris m q w

B. sylvestris m² f
B. bohemicus m f¹
B. vestalis m¹ f¹

B. hypnorum m q w

B. sylvestris f
B. lucorum m²
B. bohemicus m⁵ f⁵
B. vestalis m⁵

B. terrestris m q w¹
B. lucorum m² q w¹
B. soroeensis m³ q³ w³

B. pascuorum m² q² w²
B. muscorum m q w
B. humilis m q w

B. campestris m¹ f
B. sylvestris m² f

B. campestris m¹ f

Cuckoo bumblebees tend to have darker wings, in particular female B. rupestris and B. vestalis.

Beware colour fading in older, and usually worn, bumblebees.

B = social bumblebee
B = cuckoo, or socially parasitic, species

BOMBUS LAPIDARIUS

IDENTIFICATION

Appearance: Queens and workers: head, thorax and abdomen black with orange-red tail, which is less than 50% of length of abdomen. Abdomen longer than wide. Males: facial hairs yellow, thorax with yellow bands, abdomen black, tail orange-red. Large, robust species, although workers may be much smaller. Face as long as wide, tongue mid-length.

Variability: The extent and brightness of the yellow in males varies, with some individuals having very little yellow banding. Very occasionally females may have faint yellow banding.

Similar species: Queens and workers of the rarer *B. ruderarius* have much rounder abdomens and the hairs fringing the pollen basket of females are orange, not black. The yellow bands on the thorax of males are almost always much brighter in *B. lapidarius*. The wings of the socially parasitic species *B. rupestris* are smoky, not clear, and the abdomen of females has much less hair. If in doubt, it is useful to check the shape of the male genitalia with these three species.

DISTRIBUTION and BIOLOGY

A widespread species found in many habitats. It is currently spreading into north-eastern Scotland.

Nests: Made in a variety of situations, usually in open areas; underground or in wall cavities. Nest-searching queens can be seen from March to June, depending on the distance north. Mature nests are large and frequently contain over 150 workers. Young nests are sometimes taken over by the similarly coloured socially parasitic species *B. rupestris*. Males are often seen patrolling round isolated bushes or along hedge lines. Newly mated queens may hibernate in large numbers in traditional areas, such as north-facing banks in open woodland.

Flower visits: Seems to be very fond of yellow flowers, especially Bird's-foot-trefoils; also likes Scabiouses and Knapweeds.

44

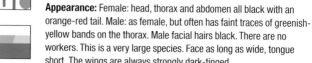

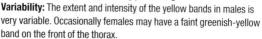

IDENTIFICATION

A cuckoo bumblebee.

Appearance: Female: head, thorax and abdomen all black with an orange-red tail. Male: as female, but often has faint traces of greenish-yellow bands on the thorax. Male facial hairs black. There are no workers. This is a very large species. Face as long as wide, tongue short. The wings are always strongly dark-tinged.

Variability: The extent and intensity of the yellow bands in males is very variable. Occasionally females may have a faint greenish-yellow band on the front of the thorax.

Similar species: *B. lapidarius* and *B. ruderarius* but the round face, lack of pollen basket on hind leg of female and darkened wings are distinctive. Males of *B. rupestris* usually have indistinct yellow bands, with elongated abdomens. If in doubt, it is useful to check the male genitalia on any of these three species.

DISTRIBUTION and BIOLOGY

A widespread species, found in many habitats in the southern half of the UK.
It has recently shown a marked increase in frequency and is moving northwards.
It is scarce and restricted in Ireland. Host-searching females may be seen in April
and May, and new females and males are often seen resting on flowers in July
and August.

Nests: This species takes over the nests of *B. lapidarius*.

Flower visits: A wide range of flowers is visited for nectar and individual
consumption of pollen. Does not collect pollen for young.

BOMBUS RUDERARIUS

46

IDENTIFICATION

Appearance: Queens and workers: all-black with orange-red tail with orange hairs on the hind tibiae. The abdomen is about as long as wide and appears almost circular as the bees fly away from you. Males: general appearance of the face and thorax black, with faint greenish-yellow bands on the thorax and pale greenish-yellow hairs among the black ones on the face; the abdomen generally appears black and tail orange-red, but there may be a band of green-yellow hairs which is preceded by a band of black hairs. Face longer than wide, tongue long.

Variability: The extent and brightness of the yellow in males varies, but overall the appearance of this sex is usually rather dull. Queens and workers show no variation.

Similar species: Queens and workers of the commoner *B. lapidarius* have much longer abdomens, the red is less orange and the hairs fringing the pollen basket are black, not orange. Males are generally brighter in *B. lapidarius*, with plentiful yellow hairs on the face. The wings of the much larger *B. rupestris* are smoky, not clear. If in doubt, it is useful to check the male genitalia with these three species.

DISTRIBUTION and BIOLOGY

A declining species, sometimes found in gardens and urban waste-ground but generally asociated with more extensive areas of taller, open grasslands and scrub. Nest-searching queens are later than those of *B. lapidarius*, being seen in April and early May in the south. Males are found in late July and early August. A very strong population exists on the Inner Hebridean Islands of Coll and Tiree, far to the north of other known populations.

Nests: Made in old mouse and vole nests at the base of large tussocks of grass. The bees collect moss to build the cover of the nest (hence carder bees). Mature nests are small, with fewer than 100 workers.

Flower visits: There is a strong preference for flowers of legumes (especially Clovers), labiates; Knapweeds and Red Bartsia.

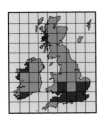

BOMBUS MONTICOLA

IDENTIFICATION

Appearance: Queens, workers and males: two yellow bands on the thorax, none on the abdomen. The rear thoracic band is often reduced in width, but not darkened. The yellow is bright and lemonish in hue. The tail is orange-red and extends over half the abdomen. The male has distinctive yellow facial hair. This is a small species. Face as long as wide, tongue short.

Variability: Very little variation.

Similar species: Males of *B. lapidarius* and all casts of *B. pratorum* (and Scottish islands form of *B. jonellus*) may be confused, but none of these has the orange tail extending over anything like as much of the abdomen.

DISTRIBUTION and BIOLOGY

A restricted species. There are no confirmed records from the SE of England, even in relatively high areas such as the High Weald of Sussex. Declining everywhere. Nest-searching queens in April.

Nests: Made at the base of tall Heather or Bilberry, sometimes just underground. Mature nests small, with fewer than 100 workers.

Flower visits: Although the plant cannot supply all the needs of *B. monticola*, there is a strong association with extensive areas of tall Bilberry, which is regularly visited for both pollen and nectar when in flower. Sallow seems to be visited for nectar rather than pollen. Bird's foot-trefoils, White Clover and Raspberry are much used during the mid-summer months. Bell-heather is much visited in late summer.

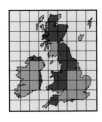
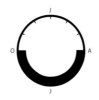

BOMBUS SYLVARUM

IDENTIFICATION

Appearance: Queens, workers and males: overall colour greeny-grey, with a distinct black band running across the thorax between the wing bases. The tail is orange-red, but this is not bright or extensive. Male facial hairs greenish-yellow. This is a small, rotund species in which workers may be particularly small. Face longer than wide, tongue long.

Variability: Specimens fade very quickly, giving an overall drab grey appearance, but the orange-red tail is usually clearly seen.

Similar species: No other species is quite the same in looks, but faded and worn workers of *B. pascuorum, B. humilis,* and *B. muscorum* can appear to have a black band between the wings where the hair has rubbed off. In *B. sylvarum* this band is made of black hairs. The other species never have an orange-red tail.

DISTRIBUTION and BIOLOGY

A very localised and declining species, now known from just five areas within the UK and very restricted in Ireland. It is extinct over much of its former range, including the entire south coast of England. It may be associated with dry or wet grasslands and is particularly associated with areas rich in labiate and legume flowers. Nest-searching queens fly relatively late in the year, not often before the beginning of May.

Nests: Made on the surface of the ground within open, but taller, vegetation. Mature nests are medium-sized, with about 100 workers.

Flower visits: Very strongly associated with flowers which are complex or have long corollae. Red Clover, Red Bartsia, Knapweeds and Woundworts are well used. The strong population along the River Thames east of London is heavily dependent upon areas of Narrow-leaved Bird's-foot-trefoil.

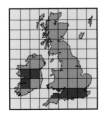

BOMBUS PRATORUM

IDENTIFICATION

Appearance: Queens, workers and males: one yellow stripe on thorax and one on the abdomen, the latter preceded by a black band. Tail orange. The male has very distinctive yellow hairs on face. This is a small species, especially the workers. Face as long as wide, tongue short.

Variability: Some individuals, especially small workers, can be very dark or almost all black. Males can be extensively yellow, including a second band on the thorax.

Similar species: *B. lapidarius* males are obviously less yellow overall, and larger, with fewer yellow facial hairs. There is a resemblance to *B. monticola* which is most marked in the males, but there is much less red on tail and the yellow bands are mid-yellow, compared with the lemon-yellow of *B. monticola*. The form of *B. jonellus* in the Western Isles and Shetland is similarly coloured, but *B. pratorum* is unknown here.

DISTRIBUTION and BIOLOGY

A widespread species, found in many habitats. A regular garden species where it is a particularly good pollinator of soft-fruit flowers. Often has two generations a year in southern areas, but this is not confirmed towards the north. Queens are among the first bumblebees of spring and males are often produced in May.

Nests: Made in a variety of situations, at ground-level in the bases of bushes, underground and in holes in trees. The nest is remarkably short-lived, with new sexuals often appearing three months after the founding queens. Mature nests are small, often with fewer than 100 workers.

Flower visits: Often seen visiting the flowers of shrubs, especially Raspberry and Bramble, but also a wide range of other plants.

BOMBUS TERRESTRIS

IDENTIFICATION

Appearance: Queens, workers and males: single yellow stripe on front of the thorax, one on the abdomen, which is preceded by a black band. Tail dirty-white to buff, occasionally orange-red. The buff tails are most noticeable in the queens, and this forms a good character to separate *B. terrestris* and *B. lucorum* queens. The facial hair of the male is black, unlike *B. lucorum*, where it is yellow. This is a very large, robust species, although workers may be much smaller. Face as long as wide, tongue very short.

Variability: There is little variability in UK-native populations, but this might change with the increasing use of captive-reared colonies of this species as pollinators in glasshouses. Over its entire range it is a very variable species.

Similar species: Whilst males and queens are easily separated from those of *B. lucorum*, separation of workers is problematic and very unreliable in the field, when it is wisest to record workers as *terrestris/lucorum*.

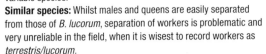

DISTRIBUTION and BIOLOGY

A common and very widespread species, found in many habitats but not in the far north and generally scarce in Scotland, although it is moving north at the time of writing. A regular garden species. Nest-searching queens are probably the first emerging bumblebee species, frequently being seen in February in the south.
Nests: Made in a variety of situations, usually underground, but always under cover. Mature nests very large, with over 300 workers.
Flower visits: Visits a very wide variety of flowers and may engage in nectar-robbing of longer-tubed flowers by cutting through the base of the corolla as the tongue is too short to reach the nectar otherwise. Spring queens, in particular, may swarm around aphid-bearing conifers where they are taking honeydew.

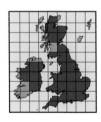

BOMBUS SOROEENSIS

IDENTIFICATION

Appearance: Queens, workers and males: one lemon-yellow stripe on the thorax and one on the abdomen. The abdominal yellow band is preceded by a black one, but the yellow band tends to creep forward at the sides of the first segment. The tail is white, often with a narrow peach band at the interface between the white and black. Male facial hairs black. This is a medium-sized species in the queen and male but workers are consistently small. Face as long as wide, tongue short.

Variability: The extent of the peach coloration is variable. It may be very extensive in some males, but it is sometimes completely missing.

Similar species: *B. lucorum* very similarly coloured, but without forward extension of yellow on the abdomen, and the tail is always pure white. Difficult examples require microscopic examination of the mandible in queens and workers, or the shape of the genitalia in males.

DISTRIBUTION and BIOLOGY

A widespread but very localised species, found in extensive areas of late-flowering plants. These may be limestone grasslands, moorlands or coastal areas. It is apparently absent from Ireland. Nest-searching queens of *B. soroeensis* are notably late flying, not being seen until June, even in the south. Males fly between August and October.

Nests: Made in a variety of situations, usually underground, but always under cover. Mature nests are medium-sized with about 100 workers.

Flower visits: Smaller-flowered legumes, especially Melilots, are frequently visited by queens and mid-summer workers. Harebell and other *Campanula* species together with Devil's-bit Scabious, are much favoured in August and September.

BOMBUS LUCORUM

IDENTIFICATION

Appearance: Queens, workers and some males: single yellow band on front of the thorax and one on the abdomen; the abdominal yellow band is preceded by a black band. The tail is white. The facial hair of the male is yellow, unlike *B. terrestris,* where it is black. The yellow is a good clear one, not muddy. This is a large and robust species, although workers may be much smaller. Face as long as wide, tongue very short.

Variability: Some males have an additional yellow band at the rear of the thorax and no black band in front of the yellow on the abdomen. There may be two further hidden species within what is called *B. lucorum: B. magnus* and *B. cryptarum.*

Similar species: Whilst males and queens are easily separated from those of *B. terrestris,* separation of workers is problematic and very unreliable in the field, when it is wisest to record workers as *terrestris/lucorum.*

DISTRIBUTION and BIOLOGY

A common and very widespread species found in many habitats, but more frequent towards the north. A regular garden species. Nest-searching queens of this species are one of the first bumblebees seen in the spring, as early as February in the south. They may even start nests in the autumn in very mild areas.

Nests: Made in a variety of situations, usually underground, but always under cover. Mature nests are large, often with over 200 workers.

Flower visits: Visits a very wide variety of flowers, and may engage in nectar-robbing of longer-tubed flowers by cutting through the base of the corolla, as the tongue is too short to reach the nectar otherwise. Spring queens, in particular, may swarm around aphid-bearing conifers where they are taking honeydew.

BOMBUS JONELLUS

IDENTIFICATION

Appearance: Queens, workers and males: two yellow bands on the thorax, one at the base of the abdomen. Tail white in mainland forms. The male has very distinctive yellow hairs on the face. The form in the Western Isles and Shetlands has an orange tail. This is a small species, especially the workers. Face as long as wide, tongue short.

Variability: Some individuals can be very dark or almost all black, especially queens. Note the orange, not white, tail in the Western Isles.

Similar species: Often overlooked, being mistaken for *B. hortorum* which is similarly coloured, but has a face which is much longer than wide and a very long tongue.

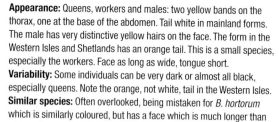

DISTRIBUTION and BIOLOGY

A widespread species found in many habitats, although particularly plentiful in heathy districts. Has two generations a year in the southern part of the UK, where queens are among the first bumblebees of spring. In the north, queens are not usually seen much before June.

Nests: Made in a variety of situations, at ground-level in the bases of bushes, underground and in holes in trees. The nest is remarkably short-lived, with new sexuals often appearing three months after the founding queens. Mature nests are rather small, containing fewer than 100 workers.

Flower visits: Sallows in the spring (and winter-flowering Heathers in gardens), a frequent visitor to Heathers in heathy areas. Uses a wide range of flowers.

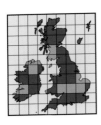

BOMBUS HORTORUM

IDENTIFICATION

Appearance: Queens, workers and males: two yellow bands on thorax and one at the base of the abdomen. Tail white. Male facial hairs black. This is a large, robust species, although early workers may be much smaller. The face is very much longer than wide, tongue is very long: it can be very obvious as the bee approaches a flower and unfolds its tongue in preparation for drinking nectar.

Variability: Some individuals can be very dark or almost all-black, but the tail usually remains white.

Similar species: Reliable separation of the rare, but very similar, *B. ruderatus* is not easy in the field and may not be possible in all individuals. All-black specimens are more likely to be *B. ruderatus*. Otherwise, probably the most reliable characters are the distribution of the yellow bands on the thorax (the front one is wider than the back one in *B. hortorum*) and the extent of the yellow abdominal band. This spreads onto the centre of the second segment of the abdomen in *B. hortorum*. *B. jonellus* is similarly coloured, but has a face which is as long as wide and is generally smaller.

DISTRIBUTION and BIOLOGY

A widespread species found in many habitats. It may not be frequent in any particular area. A garden species.

Nests: Made in a variety of situations, usually underground, but always under cover. Nest-searching queens may be seen from March to early May. Mature nests are medium sized, containing about 100 workers. Young nests may be taken over by the very similarly coloured *B. barbutellus*. The first males are often found in June. These are often found visiting the same kinds of flowers as workers.

Flower visits: One of two common species which regularly visit Foxglove flowers, the other being *B. pascuorum*. It also frequently uses Red Clover and Dead-nettles. Generally associated with flowers which are complex or have long corollae.

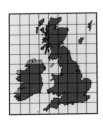

BOMBUS RUDERATUS

IDENTIFICATION

Appearance: Queens, workers and males: the typical striped form has two yellow stripes on the thorax and one on the abdomen, and the yellow is bright-mustard in hue. The front and back thoracic stripes are equal in width, front to back, in all striped forms. The yellow hairs on the abdomen are on the first segment only. The tail is white. Male facial hairs black. This is a large, robust species, although workers may be rather smaller. Face very much longer than wide, tongue very long.

Variability: The extent and intensity of the yellow stripes is very variable. Some individuals can be very dark or even all black. Darker individuals have muddier white tails than strongly yellow ones.

Similar species: Reliable separation of the common, but very similar, *B. hortorum* is not easy in the field and may not be possible in all individuals. All-black specimens are more likely to be *B. ruderatus*. *B. jonellus* is similarly coloured, but has a face as long as wide, and is generally smaller.

DISTRIBUTION and BIOLOGY

A scarce and declining species, possibly associated with wetland habitats. There is much to learn about the ecology of this species. Nest-searching queens have been seen in April and May.

Nests: Made underground, as far as is known. Mature nests are reportedly large, with over 150 workers.

Flower visits: The difficulty of reliably identifying this species means that there is little detailed information. However, it is generally associated with flowers which are complex or have long corollae, such as Clovers or Dead-nettles. It is one of three species which visit Foxglove (the others being the widespread *B. hortorum* and *B. pascuorum*). It is also frequently seen at Yellow Iris and Comfries in wetland localities.

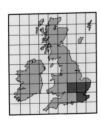

IDENTIFICATION

A cuckoo bumblebee.

Appearance: Females and males: two yellow stripes on the thorax, one on the abdomen. The tail is white. There are no workers. This species attacks *B. hortorum*, which it closely resembles. It is generally darker, with sparser hairs and darkened wings. This is a large species. Face as long as wide. The facial hairs of the male are black.

Variability: Some individuals can be very dark or almost all-black.

Similar species: Most like its host, *B. hortorum*, but the face being as long as wide and lack of pollen basket on the hind leg of the female are distinctive features.

DISTRIBUTION and BIOLOGY

A widespread species found in many habitats, although not, apparently, as widespread as its host. This is particularly obvious in the Irish distribution. Females searching for hosts are seen in April and May and new males and females are often seen sitting around on flowers in July and August.

Nests: This species takes over the nests of *B. hortorum* and, probably, *B. ruderatus*.

Flower visits: A wide range of flowers is visited for nectar and individual consumption of pollen. Does not collect pollen for young.

BOMBUS BOHEMICUS

IDENTIFICATION

A cuckoo bumblebee.

Appearance: Females: one mid-yellow band on thorax, none on abdomen. Males: facial hairs black, two yellow bands on thorax, usually none on abdomen. Tail white with small mid-yellow side patches at junction with black in both sexes. There are no workers. This species attacks *B. lucorum,* to which it looks quite similar. It is a large robust species. Face as long as wide, tongue short. The wings are strongly dark-tinged.

Variability: Very variable, especially males. There may be a faint yellow band at the front of the abdomen. Sometimes the tail is ginger in males.

Similar species: *B. vestalis* is very similar but the yellow is darker and the side patches larger.

DISTRIBUTION and BIOLOGY

A widespread species, found in many habitats. It is noticeably commoner towards the north.

Nests: This species takes over the nests of *B. lucorum*. Females searching for hosts are seen in April and May and new males and females are often seen resting on flowers in July and August.

Flower visits: A wide range of flowers is visited for nectar and individual consumption of pollen. Does not collect pollen for young.

70

IDENTIFICATION

A cuckoo bumblebee.

Appearance: Females and males: one dark-yellow stripe on the thorax, none on the abdomen. The tail is white, with clear, dark-yellow side patches at the junction with the black. The wings are usually strongly dark-tinged. Male facial hairs black. There are no workers. This is a large, robust species. Face as long as wide, tongue short.

Variability: Very variable, especially males. There may be an additional faint yellow band at the base of the abdomen.

Similar species: *B. bohemicus* is very similar, but the yellow is lighter and the side patches smaller.

DISTRIBUTION and BIOLOGY

A widespread species, found in many habitats in England and Wales. In southern districts this is easily the most often found cuckoo bumblebee species. It is only recently known from Scotland and is not currently known from Ireland. Host-searching females may be out as early as late March. New females and males may be seen resting on flowers from June to August.

Nests: This species takes over the nests of *B. terrestris*.

Flower visits: A wide range of flowers is visited for nectar and individual consumption of pollen. Does not collect pollen for young.

BOMBUS SYLVESTRIS

72

IDENTIFICATION

A cuckoo bumblebee.

Appearance: Females and males: (in the commonest form) one yellow stripe on the thorax, one on the abdomen. The tail is white, but this is followed by a narrow tip of black. In males there are a few orange hairs at the very tip. In females the end of the abdomen is very curled-under (hold the specimen in a tube to check this). Male facial hairs black. There are no workers. This is a small species. Face as long as wide, tongue short. The wings are usually strongly dark-tinged.

Variability: There may be an additional yellow band on the base of the abdomen and/or thorax, especially in males. Sometimes the tail is ginger-yellow.

Similar species: Males of *B. campestris* are somewhat similar to those of *B. sylvestris*. However, the very tip of the tail of *B. campestris* males has black hairs whilst these hairs are orange in *B. sylvestris* males.

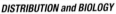

DISTRIBUTION and BIOLOGY

A widespread species, found in many habitats. Host-searching females may be seen from April through to June, or even July. At least one host species can be double-brooded in the south and, in such situations, *B. sylvestris* may also be double-brooded. New females and males may be seen resting on flowers from June to August.

Nests: This species takes over the nests of *B. pratorum,* and probably attacks both *B. jonellus* and *B. monticola.*

Flower visits: A wide range of flowers is visited for nectar and individual consumption of pollen. Does not collect pollen for young.

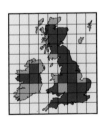

BOMBUS HYPNORUM

IDENTIFICATION

Appearance: Queens, workers and males: head black, thorax tawny to dark-brown, abdomen black with white tail. Male facial hairs black. The queens and males are medium-sized and rotund, workers are rather small. Face as long as wide, tongue short.

Variability: The distribution of tawny-brown and black hairs is quite variable, with some specimens very dark and some predominantly tawny. The extent of white on the tail is variable, but this is always present.

Similar species: Some examples of *B. pascuorum* have large areas of black on the abdomen, but do not have a white tail. This white tail can be readily observed as the bee flies away from the observer.

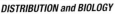

DISTRIBUTION and BIOLOGY

Newly found in the UK in 2000; this species has been expanding its range steadily in 'mainland' Europe. It seems to have a close affinity with urban and woodland habitats throughout Europe, where it is widely distributed. It is expected that *B. hypnorum* will spread widely in the UK. It is possible that this species is double-brooded, with nest-searching queens in March and again in June. New females appear from the end of May to September.

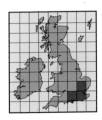

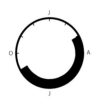

BOMBUS CAMPESTRIS

IDENTIFICATION

A cuckoo bumblebee.

Appearance: Females and males: (in the commonest form) two yellow stripes on the thorax, none on the abdomen. Tail with greenish-yellow side patches which are quite extensive, frequently being up to half the length of the abdomen. Male facial hairs black. There are no workers. This is a medium-sized species. Face as long as wide, tongue short. The wings are often strongly dark-tinged.

Variability: Very variable, especially males. There may be an additional faint yellow band at the rear of the thorax and also one on the abdomen. At the extremes of variation individuals can be very dark, almost all-black, or the side patches may extend over almost all the abdomen.

Similar species: Males of *B. sylvestris* are somewhat similar to those of *B. campestris*. However, the very tip of the tail of *B. campestris* males has black hairs whilst these hairs are orange in *B. sylvestris* males.

DISTRIBUTION and BIOLOGY

A widespread species, found in many habitats. Host-searching females may be seen in April and May and new females and males are often seen sitting around on flowers in July and August.

Nests: This species takes over the nests of *B. pascuorum* and probably attacks all the carder bumblebees (*B. humilis, B. muscorum, B. ruderarius* and *B. sylvarum*).

Flower visits: A wide range of flowers is visited for nectar and individual consumption of pollen. Does not collect pollen for young.

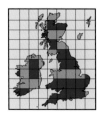

BOMBUS DISTINGUENDUS

IDENTIFICATION

Appearance: Queens, workers and males: pale mustard-yellow all over, with a distinct, almost parallel-sided, band of black hairs running across the thorax between the bases of the wings. A large, robust species, although early workers may be much smaller. Face very much longer than wide, tongue long. Male facial hairs black and yellow.

Variability: Very little.

Similar species: None among currently known UK species, although males of *B. subterraneus* (now considered extinct in the UK) are very similar. Care needs to be taken with worn *B. humilis, B. muscorum* and *B. pascuorum,* which may appear to have a black band between the wings. Close inspection will show this to be due to a LACK of hairs, and is actually the hard chitin showing through.

DISTRIBUTION and BIOLOGY

A very restricted and declining species, which is commonest in flower-rich, extensive grasslands, such as tall machair in the Western Isles. It may also be present in other flower-rich habitats in northern mainland Scotland and the Orkneys.
Nests: Made in a variety of situations, usually underground, but always under cover. Mature nests are rather small, containing fewer than 100 workers. Nest-searching queens may be seen from the end of May to early July. In the Hebrides these show a strong preference for the flowers of Bird's-foot-trefoils.
Flower visits: A very strong association with the flowers of Red Clover, if these are available in the area. Also frequent at other legume flowers, such as White Clover and Bird's-foot-trefoils; Marsh Woundwort, Marsh Thistle and Knapweeds.

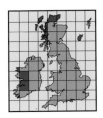
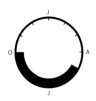

BOMBUS PASCUORUM

IDENTIFICATION

Appearance: Queens, workers and males: almost entirely pale ginger-brown, but with variable patches of black hairs on the abdomen; sometimes these are very extensive. There are also distinct black hairs among the ginger-brown ones of the thorax. Male facial hairs ginger-brown. A medium-sized species. The abdomen is almost round, but appears more ovoid in males. Face longer than wide, tongue long. Males can be confirmed easily by examination of genitalia.

Variability: Little basic variability apart from the extent of the black hairs on the sides of the abdomen, although the hairs often fade to almost grey-brown. Note that some specimens may have very few black hairs, especially in Scotland; these require careful checking.

Similar species: Very easily confused with *B. humilis* and *B. muscorum* if the black patches are very reduced (microscopic examination only). If found in woodland situations it is most likely to be *B. pascuorum*.

DISTRIBUTION and BIOLOGY

A widespread species found in many habitats. A regular garden species. The range of this species is expanding at the moment. Nest-searching queens are the earliest of the carder-bees to be seen, often in March in the south.

Nests: Made in a variety of situations but usually on or just under the ground. The bees collect moss to build the cover of the nest (hence carder-bee). Mature nests are medium-sized, with about 100 workers.

Flower visits: Although this species will visit a fairly wide range of flowers it is very fond of the flowers of legumes and Dead-nettles. It is one of two common species which regularly visits the flowers of Foxgloves (the other being *B. hortorum*).

BOMBUS HUMILIS

(M)

IDENTIFICATION

Appearance: Queens, workers and males: entirely pale ginger-brown, although the thorax may be rather darker in hue. Male facial hairs pale ginger-brown. This is a relatively small species and the workers may be particularly small. When examined closely, a few black hairs can be seen on the thorax just above the base of the wings (hold the specimen in a tube to check this). There are NEVER any black hairs on the sides of the abdomen. Face longer than wide, tongue long. Males can be easily confirmed by examination of genitalia.

Variability: Little basic variability, but the hairs often fade to almost grey-brown.

Similar species: Very easily confused with the commonly found *B. pascuorum* (black hairs on abdomen) and the scarce *B. muscorum* (microscopic examination only). The brown band on the abdomen is unreliable for separating *B. humilis* and *B. muscorum*. The hairs are less dense than in *B. muscorum*, which often has a more velvety appearance.

DISTRIBUTION and BIOLOGY

The southern half of Britain; Anglesey is the northernmost locality. It is absent
from Ireland. Strongly associated with tall, but open, flower-rich grasslands, often
coastal. A declining species.

Nests: Almost invariably on the surface in tall, but not rank, grassland with the top
of the nest open to the sun. The mature nest is small, often with considerably fewer
than 100 workers. The bees use moss raked (hence carder-bee) from the litter layer
to make the nest covering.

Flower visits: A strong preference for the flowers of legumes (especially Clovers),
labiates, Knapweeds and Red Bartsia. The bees seek out scattered flowers within
the taller grasslands, rather than visiting large stands growing in the open.

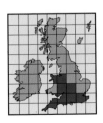

BOMBUS MUSCORUM

IDENTIFICATION

Appearance: Queens, workers and males: entirely pale ginger-brown, although the thorax is rather darker in hue compared with the abdomen. The coat appears dense and very even, giving it a velvety texture in fresh specimens. Male facial hairs ginger-brown. This is a medium-sized species. When examined closely there are NO black hairs to be seen on the thorax just above the base of the wings. There are NEVER any black hairs on the sides of the abdomen. Face longer than wide, tongue long. Males can be easily confirmed by examination of genitalia.

Variability: Little variation but the hairs often fade to almost grey-brown. Forms with black hair on the face and lower parts occur on some islands.

Similar species: Very easily confused with the commonly found *B. pascuorum* (black hairs on abdomen, but these may be very few, especially in the north) and *B. humilis* (microscopic examination only). The presence or absence of a brown band on the abdomen is unreliable.

DISTRIBUTION and BIOLOGY

Throughout, but more frequent towards the north and west. Strongly associated with tall, but open, flower-rich grasslands, often coastal. It is associated with wetter sites in the south, where its range overlaps that of the closely related *B. humilis*. A severely declining species. Nest-searching queens are rarely seen before May.

Nests: Almost invariably on the surface, in tall, but not rank grassland, with the top of the nest open to the sun. The bees use moss raked (hence carder-bee) from the litter layer to make the nest covering. Mature nests are small, with under 100 workers.

Flower visits: A strong preference for flowers of legumes (especially Clovers), labiates, Knapweeds and Red Bartsia. The bees seek out scattered flowers within the taller grasslands, rather than visit large stands growing in the open.

GARDENS AND BUMBLEBEES

Bumblebees are attractive, harmless insects, which can be a source of interest and enjoyment – especially to children. They are also essential for the pollination of fruit trees, soft fruits, beans and flowers, and are able to pollinate at much lower temperatures than other bees and insects. Bumblebees' presence, along with their buzzing sound, adds another dimension and harmony to any garden – especially when complemented by other types of wild life.

With change in farming practices and the consequent loss of wild plant communities, gardens have become an important component of wildlife habitats. Some animal species such as the Hedgehog *Erinaceus europaeus*, Common Frog *Rana temporaria* and Common Toad *Bufo bufo* now have higher population densities in gardens than the surrounding countryside.

The situation is much better, too, for those bumblebee species which can complete their life cycles in gardens. The six commonest bumblebees: *Bombus terrestris*, *B. lapidarius*, *B. hortorum*, *B. pratorum*, *B. pascuorum* and *B. lucorum* now often have higher population densities in urban environments than in the countryside. These commoner species of bumblebee collect their food from a wider variety of flowers, and the provision of a continual forage source in gardens clearly has a positive effect on their populations.

The higher density of the commoner species of bumblebee – and other animals – in gardens is good news as it illustrates the importance of gardens as a wildlife habitat and as a biodiversity resource. There are over 25 million households in Britain, an estimated 15 million of these having gardens. A recent study by Sheffield University gives considerable detail of this. See: Gaston, J *et al.*, 2004. Gardens and wildlife – the Bugs project. *British Wildlife* **16**; No 1, 1-9. It highlights the potential influence of gardens on the total number of species and individuals (biomass) in Britain and Ireland. The increasing interest by the general public in natural history and wildlife gardening bodes well for the future, whilst providing the opportunity for many people to play an active and independent role in conservation.

Male *Bombus terrestris*.

GARDENING FOR BUMBLEBEES

The provision of a varied and continual supply of nectar and pollen is obviously critical for the success of a bumblebee colony and the British love affair with their gardens has been of great benefit to them. However, fashions change: there is not much value in decking or tightly mown grass; or planting conifers. Nor are many of the highly bred double flowers much use to bumblebees, as their pollen and nectar parts have often been sacrificed for more petals as a result of breeding. Some introduced garden plants are naturally pollinated by bats or birds, rather than insects.

To attract foraging bumblebees to your garden it is important to provide a range of suitable plants with flowering times that cover the whole of the bumblebee season – ideally from February to September. Growing single flowers, particular those with close relatives in wild flora, is the best option. Several National Trust gardeners have also recently decided to grow just single-flowered Dahlias for formal bedding, having noticed how popular these are with *Bombus terrestris*! Traditional cottage garden plants, which include many that are related to native flora, such as Foxgloves, Honeysuckles, Campanulas, Scabiouses, Poppies, and Geraniums (Cranesbills), are very good for bumblebees, too. There are also a number of flowering shrubs that are excellent forage plants for bumblebees, and are especially important during the beginning and the end of the season. The table overleaf lists suitable garden plants and their flowering times. Those that are highlighted with ∗ are particularly effective in attracting bumblebees and it is a good idea to make sure at least two of these are flowering at any one time.

Male *Bombus hortorum* on Delphinium.

Male *Bombus lucorum* on Astrantia.

Many of the wild flowers that bumblebees love are closely related to some of our familiar garden plants so you can easily substitute the wild version for the garden version in a flower bed. Alternatively, you can create a wild flower garden or meadow with bumblebees in mind. The table overleaf lists those wild flowers which are preferred by bumblebees and at the back of the book is a list of suppliers where they can be purchased, if you cannot find them locally.

When creating a wild flower meadow for bumblebees there are a number of tips you may find useful:

- Bumblebees are sun-loving insects so for the best results your chosen site should be in a well sheltered sunny location.

- Scattering wild flower seeds on grassland is not cost effective – few plants will germinate. It is better to plant seeds in bare soil or germinate them in trays for planting out.

- It is more effective to use potted plants when planting straight into a grassy area, and it is also a good idea to mow this before planting.

- If you are planting a large grassy area, you can purchase trays of plantlets – individually called plugs – which are much cheaper.

- It is a good idea to mow your wild flower meadow once the plants have become established, the flowers have blossomed and all their seeds have matured – usually in the late autumn. The cuttings should be removed, not left on the ground.

Table 1. Bumblebee garden plants for all seasons

	Common Name	Botanical Name	Star plant
March – April			
	Bluebell	Endymion	
	Barberry	Berberis	*
	Bugle	Ajuga	
	Cowslip	Primula	
	Crocus	Crocus	
	Dead-nettle	Lamium	*
	Flowering Currant	Ribes	*
	Forget-me-not	Myosotis	
	Gorse	Ulex	
	Heathers	Erica	
	Lungwort	Pulmonaria	*
	Mexican Orange	Choisya	
	Plum	Prunus	*
	Rhododendron	Rhododendron	*
	Rosemary	Rosmarinus	*
May – June			
	Apple	Malus	
	Bellflower	Campanula	
	Borage	Borago	
	Ceaonothus	Ceaonothus	
	Chives	Allium	
	Colombine	Aquilegia	*
	Comfrey	Symphytum	*
	Crab Apple	Malus	
	Crane's-bill	Geranium	*
	Everlasting Pea	Lathyrus	*
	Fleabane	Erigeron	
	Foxglove	Digitalis	*
	Hawthorn	Crataegus	*
	Honeysuckle	Lonicera	
	Lamb's-tongue	Stachys	
	Poppy	Papaver	
	Thyme	Thymus	*
July – August			
	Apple Blossom	Escallonia	
	Cornflower	Centaurea	*
	Delphinium	Delphinium	*
	Firethorn	Pyracantha	
	Globe Thistle	Echinops	*
	Hebe	Hebe	*
	Jasmine (Summer)	Jasminum	
	Lavender	Lavandula	*
	Marjoram	Origanum	*
	Masterwort	Astrantia	
	Rock-rose	Helianthemum	*
	Scabious	Scabiosa	*
	Sea Holly	Eryngium	*
	Verbena	Verbena	

Table 2. Bumblebee wild flowers for all seasons

	Common Name	Scientific Name	Star plant
March – April			
	Blackthorn	*Prunus spinosa*	
	Bluebell	*Endymion non-scriptus*	
	Cowslip	*Primula veris*	
	Gorse	*Ulex europaeus*	
	Ground Ivy	*Glechoma hederacea*	☆
	Pussy Willow	*Salix caprea*	☆
	White Dead-nettle	*Lamium album*	☆
	Yellow Archangel	*Lamiastrum galeobdolon*	☆
May – June			
	Bird's-foot-trefoil	*Lotus corniculatus*	☆
	Bush Vetch	*Vicia sepium*	☆
	Bugle	*Ajuga repans*	☆
	Broom	*Cytisus scoparius*	
	Foxglove	*Digitalis purpurea*	☆
	Hawthorn	*Crataegus monogyna*	
	Horseshoe Vetch	*Hippocrepis comosa*	
	Meadow Vetchling	*Lathyrus pratense*	☆
	Red Clover	*Trifolium pratense*	☆
	White Bryony	*Bryonia cretica*	
	White Clover	*Trifolium repens*	☆
	Yellow Flag	*Iris pseudacorus*	
	Yellow Rattle	*Rhinanthus minor*	☆
July – August			
	Betony	*Stachys officinalis*	
	Clustered Bellflower	*Campanula glomerata*	
	Dyer's Greenweed	*Genista tinctoria*	
	Field Scabious	*Knautia arvensis*	☆
	Greater Knapweed	*Centaurea scabiosa*	☆
	Harebell	*Campanula rotundifolia*	
	Hedge Woundwort	*Stachys sylvatica*	☆
	Honeysuckle	*Lonicera pericyclymenum*	
	Lesser Knapweed	*Centaurea nigra*	☆
	Lucerne	*Medicago sativa*	☆
	Marjoram	*Origanum vulgare*	☆
	Marsh Woundwort	*Stachys palustris*	☆
	Meadow Crane's-bill	*Geranium pratense*	☆
	Melilot	*Melilotus species*	☆
	Musk Thistle	*Carduus nutans*	☆
	Nettle-leaved Bellflower	*Campanula trachelium*	
	Red Clover	*Trifolium pratense*	☆
	Sainfoin	*Onbrychis viciifolia*	
	Self-heal	*Prunella vulgaris*	
	Small Scabious	*Scabiosa columbaria*	
	Spear Thistle	*Cirsium vulgare*	
	Stemless Thistle	*Cirsium acaule*	
	Purple Loosestrife	*Lythrum sailcaria*	
	Tufted Vetch	*Vicia cracca*	☆
	Viper's Bugloss	*Echium vulgare*	☆
	White Clover	*Trifolium repens*	☆
	Wild Chives	*Allium schoenoprasum*	

Bumblebees will also nest in gardens but encouraging them to do so is a little more problematic. The best method is to leave an area of uncut rough grassland over the winter and summer months – part of a wild flower meadow is perfect – this will attract voles (whose nests bumblebees often use) and surface nesting bumblebees such as *Bombus pascuorum*. You will need to leave an uncut area of at least 2 x 5 sq metres; if any narrower than this, the nesting area should be connected to either a hedge row or rough undergrowth so that mammals can gain safe access to it. Ideally, the area selected should be cut on a rotational basis, every two or three years, to avoid it becoming too overgrown.

We have found laying down a sheet of corrugated tin on rough grassland, although a little unsightly, to be very successful for nesting bumblebees. Doing this in the late autumn, ready for the next season, is best. It is also excellent for other wildlife such as voles, shrews, grass snakes and slow worms. When the dried vegetation beneath the tin disappears – usually after one or two years – you will need to move it to another area of rough grassland.

You can create potential bumblebee nests using a handful of moss and kapok (or other natural plant fibre) and placing it in wall cavities, tree crevices, holes in banks or beneath up-turned flower pots. You can also purchase purpose-made bumblebee nests. However, bumblebees seem to be very fussy in choosing their nest sites and bumblebee nest boxes seems to have a limited success rate.

So far, identification of bumblebees using this book has been based on observing hair colouring and structural characters using live specimens. This section is designed to help you resolve some of the more problematic identifications, which are usually within the realms of experts.

Structural characters which can be used in determining bumblebees in other works refer to features such as female sting sheaths, the surface structure from which the hairs arise, malar ratios (distances between the compound eye and mandible), and surface punctuation.

As a starting point, we deal with two characters which are extremely useful: the male genitalia and the presence or absence of a spine on the mid basitarsus of the female. Both these characters require the examination and comparison of still specimens under a good hand lens or binocular microscope. For this purpose you will need a dead specimen. This may be a pinned museum specimen, one which you have found dead or one which you have killed for the purpose.

Bumblebees should only be killed for scientific reasons and great restraint should be used when considering killing queens, which are the founders of colonies. At the other end of the scale, the restrained killing of individual males doesn't threaten viable populations of bumblebees. Hence using male genitalia to confirm difficult identifications is worth considering. The killing of individual workers at the end of a season also has relatively little impact upon a colony and restrained sampling can be scientifically defensible.

Killing method
The safest and most humane method of killing bumblebees is to put individual bumblebees in glass tubes in a domestic freezer for 2 hours.

Preparing specimens for examination
This is best done by passing a long No 3 entomological pin (see Useful addresses at the back of this book on page 104) from top to bottom through the centre of the thorax (see page 95).

Spine or absence of spine on the female mid basitarsus

The mid basitarsus is immediately below the middle hind tibia. The spine, when present, is situated on the base and to the rear of the female mid basitarsus (view from the side). This is blunter, thicker and may be partially obscured by the, usually longer, surrounding hairs. The spine is present on the following female social bumblebees in the UK: *Bombus hortorum*, *B. ruderatus*, *B. ruderarius*, *B. pascuorum*, *B. muscorum*, *B. humilis*, *B. sylvarum*, *B. distinguendus*, *B. subterraneus* (now declared extinct) and all the female cuckoo bumblebees.

Mid basitasus of a female *Bombus hortorum* showing spine.

Mid basitarsus of a female cuckoo bumblebee *Bombus vestalis* showing spine.

Mid basitarsus of a female social bumblebee *Bombus jonellus* showing absence of a spine.

Extracting male genitalia

When the specimen is fresh or relaxed, you can extract these with a fine pair of entomological tweezers or a hooked pin, which you insert between the top and bottom plates of the last segments of the abdomen. You can relax old or dry specimens of bumblebees by placing them in an airtight container, with a tissue that has a few drops of water on it, for twenty four hours. Do not leave them in the container for longer than twenty four hours as they can decompose and fall apart or go mouldy. Also, make sure that the bumblebee is not in contact with the tissue.

Extracting the male genitalia

View the genitalia from above and in front of the bumblebee, and then compare to the following photographs. Related species are grouped together (known as taxonomic order). Social bumblebees are marked in black and cuckoos in red. Note the genitalia from specimens may vary within a species. This is either due to the drying process after the male has died or whether it had mated or not.

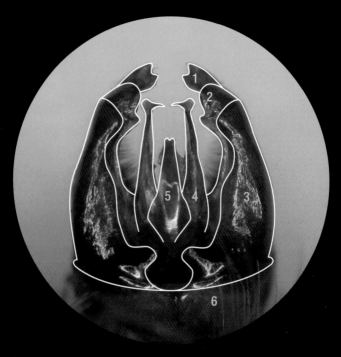

Bombus lapidarius

The structural parts of a social bumblebee's genitalia

1 Volsella
2 Squama
3 Stipes
4 Sagitta
5 Spatha
6 Cardo

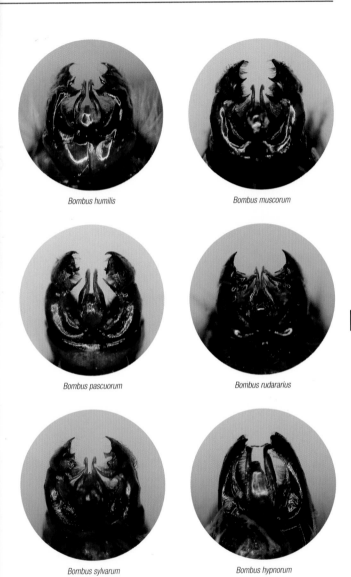

Bombus humilis

Bombus muscorum

Bombus pascuorum

Bombus rudararius

Bombus sylvarum

Bombus hypnorum

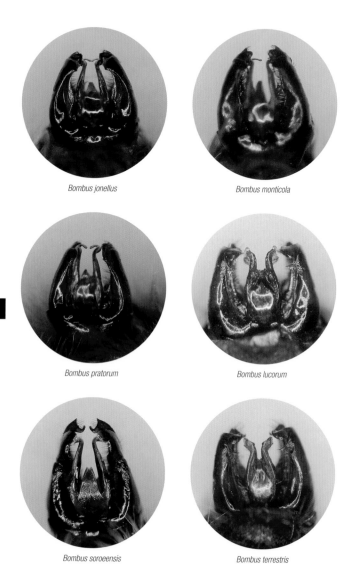

Bombus jonellus

Bombus monticola

Bombus pratorum

Bombus lucorum

Bombus soroeensis

Bombus terrestris

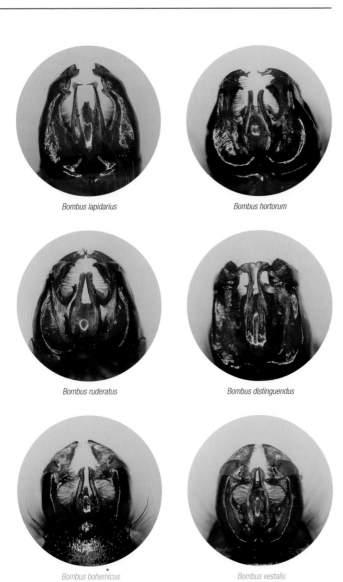

Bombus lapidarius

Bombus hortorum

Bombus ruderatus

Bombus distinguendus

Bombus bohemicus

Bombus vestalis

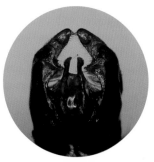

Bombus barbutellus

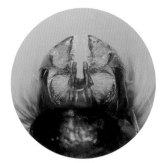

Bombus campestris

Bombus rupestris

Bombus sylvestris

Table of names for bumblebee species (Table 3)

There have been several attempts at providing common names for bumblebees, e.g. Sladen, 1912 and Step, 1932. Sladen did not give common names to the cuckoo bumblebees. Interestingly, both these authors knew them as humblebees, or carder-bees, not bumblebees!

As part of the Biodiversity Action Plan it was decided that all target species must have a common name, and in response, Macdonald, 2003 attempted to standardise them.

There have been six major works concerned (at least in part) with the bumblebees of these islands (Saunders, 1896; Sladen, 1912; Step, 1932; Butler & Free, 1959; Alford, 1975 and Prys-Jones & Corbett, 1987) as well as several regional studies. Both the scientific and the common names used in these texts have been compiled in the following table, together with comments on their derivation or appropriateness (adapted, with kind permission, from M. Macdonald, 2003, 'Bumblebees', SNH).

Where there is more than one scientific name which has been used for the same species (called synonyms) there is an accepted method to keep track of these around the world. There is no such system to monitor the use of common names (and other languages have their local common names).

Scientific name (in alphabetical order)	synonyms (G. = Genus)	English name(s)	Comment on English name
B. barbutellus	G. Psithyrus quadricolor	Barbut's Cuckoo-bee (Step) (Macdonald)	Direct translation of Latin
B. bohemicus	G. Psithyrus distinctus	Gypsy Cuckoo-bee (Step) (Macdonald)	Indirect translation of Latin: bohemian = gypsy
B. campestris	G. Psithyrus	Field Cuckoo-bee (Step) (Macdonald)	Direct translation of Latin
B. distinguendus		Great Yellow Humble-bee (Sladen) (Step) Great Yellow Bumblebee (BAP) (Macdonald)	Not the only large, yellowish species
B. humilis	helferanus solstitialis venustus	Brown-banded Carder-bee (Sladen) (Step) (BAP)	Not the only brown-banded species, especially so in queens
B. hortorum		Small Garden Humble-bee (Sladen) (Step) Garden Bumblebee (Macdonald)	Much larger than many other 'garden' species and not confined to gardens
B. hypnorum		none	
B. jonellus		Heath Humble-bee (Sladen) (Step) Heath Bumblebee (Macdonald)	But found in many more habitats

Scientific name (in alphabetical order)	synonyms (G. = Genus)	English name(s)	Comment on English name
B. lapidarius		Stone Humble-bee (Sladen) Large Red-tailed Humble-bee (Step) Red-tailed Bumblebee (Macdonald)	No clear connection with stones; queens are large and red-tailed but workers are often small; not the only red-tailed species
B. lucorum		Small Earth Humble-bee (Sladen) (Step) White-tailed Bumblebee (Macdonald)	Not one of our smaller species; not the only white-tailed species
B. monticola	lapponicus	Mountain Humble-bee (Sladen) Bilberry Humble-bee (Step)	Not the only mountain-living, or bilberry-visiting, bumblebee
B. muscorum		Large Carder-bee (Sladen) Moss Carder-bee (Step) (Macdonald)	Difficult to tell without direct comparison; not true in workers; not the only species which uses moss for its nest
B. pascuorum	agrorum	Common Carder-bee (Sladen) (Step) (Macdonald)	It is the commonest carder-bee species
B. pratorum		Early-nesting Humble-bee (Sladen) Early Humble-bee (Step) Early Bumblebee (Macdonald)	No longer the earliest-nesting species and may have a summer generation
B. ruderarius	derhamellus	Red-shanked Carder-bee (Sladen) (Step) (Macdonald)	Does have red hairs forming the pollen-basket of the hind leg
B. ruderatus		Large Garden Humble-bee (Sladen) (Step) Large Garden Bumblebee (BAP)	Large, yes, but hardly especially connected with gardens
B. rupestris	G. Psithyrus	Hill Cuckoo-bee (Step)	A lowland species
B. soroeensis	soroensis	Ilfracombe Humble-bee (Sladen) Broken-belted Humble-bee (Step) Broken-belted Bumblebee (Macdonald)	Where Edward Saunders found it; the 'broken belt' is a very difficult character to see
B. subterraneus	latreillus	Short-haired Humble-bee (Sladen) (Step) Short-haired Bumblebee (BAP)	Probably appropriate, but now extinct
B. sylvarum		Shrill Carder-bee (Sladen) (BAP) Knapweed Carder-bee (Step)	Other small species are also shrill in flight – and also visit knapweed
B. sylvestris	G. Psithyrus	Four-coloured Cuckoo-bee (Step) Forest Cuckoo-bee (Macdonald)	A good description of the abdomen banding of males – in some forms; not especially found in forests
B. terrestris		Large Earth Humble-bee (Sladen) Buff-tailed Humble-bee (Step) Buff-tailed Bumblebee (Macdonald)	Large, perhaps, especially queens and males, but not the only one; usually only buff in queens and some males
B. vestalis	G. Psithyrus	Vestal Cuckoo-bee (Step)	Direct translation of Latin

Opposite: Female *Bombus sylvestris*.

Plants:
British Wildflower Plants, Burlingham Gardens, 31 Main Road, North Burlingham, Norfolk, NR13 4TA. T. 01603 716615, E. office@wildflowers.co.uk

Emorsgate Seeds, Limes Farm, Tilney All Saints, Kings Lynn, PE34 4RT. T. 01553 829028.

Cotswold Seeds (agricultural legume mixes), Moreton In The Marsh, Gloucester. GL56 0JQ. T. 01608 652552.

Flora Locale provide a list of native wild plant and seed suppliers http://floralocale.westcountrybusinessassociates

Entomological suppliers:
Lydie Rigout, Hillside Avenue, Canterbury, Kent CT2 8ET. www.insects.demon.co.uk

Queen marking cages for handling bumblebees safely:
E. H. Thorne (beehives) Ltd, Beehive Works, Wragby, Market Rasen, Lincs., LN8 5LA. T. 01673 858555. www.thorne.co.uk

Watkins and Doncaster, PO Box 5, Cranbrook, Kent, TN18 5EZ. T. 01580 753133 email: sales@watdon www.watdon.com

Books and magazines:
British Wildlife, The Old Dairy, Milton on Stour, Gillingham, Dorset SP8 5PX. T. 01747 835511

Pemberley Books, PO Box 2081, IVER, SL0 9AZ. T. 01753 631114. www.pembooks.demon.co.uk

Societies:
Bees Wasps and Ants Recording Society. Membership Secretary, David Baldock, Nightingales, Milford, Surrey GU8 5BN. www.bwars.com.

British Entomological and Natural History Society. Membership Secretary, Andy Godfrey, 90 Bence Lane, Darton, Barnsley, South Yorkshire S75 5DA.

RSPB. The Lodge, Sandy, Beds. SG19 2DL.

Opposite: Male *Bombus lucorum*.

Further Reading

Edwards, M. and Williams P., 2004. 'Where have all the Bumblebees gone, and could they ever return?' *British Wildlife* Volume 15, number 5.

Goulson, D., 2003. *Bumblebees, their behaviour and ecology*, Oxford University Press.

Free, J and Butler, C., 1959. *Bumblebees,* New Naturalist 40. Out of print but well worth reading.

Benton, T., 2000. *The Bumblebees of Essex*, Lopinga Books.

Benton, T., *British Bumblebees.* New Naturalist HarperCollins. In print – hopefully 2005. A comprehensive work, over 200 photographs, many on bumblebee behaviour.

Sladen, F., 1912. *The Humblebee, Facsimile Edition* Logaston Press 1989. Out of print. The first major work on bumblebees, well worth a read.

Prys-Jones, O. and Corbet, S., 1987. *Bumblebees*, Naturalist's handbooks 6.

English Nature provide a number of very useful leaflets.
Listed below are some of these:

Help save the bumblebee… get more buzz from the countryside
Help save the bumblebee… get more buzz from your garden
Wildflower meadows: how to create one in your garden
Plants for wildlife-friendly gardens
Wildlife-friendly gardening

All the above leaflets can be obtained free from:
English Nature Enquiries, Northminster House, Peterborough PE1 1UA.
www.english-nature.org.uk